Water Meters—
Selection, Installation, Testing, and Maintenance

AWWA MANUAL M6

Fifth Edition

American Water Works Association

Manual of Water Supply Practices — M6, Fifth Edition

Water Meters—Selection, Installation, Testing, and Maintenance

AWWA Publications Manager: Gay Porter De Nileon
AWWA Project Manager/Sr. Technical Editor: Martha Ripley Gray
AWWA Sr. Production Editor: Cheryl Armstrong
AWWA Manuals Specialist: Molly Beach
AWWA Manuals Coordinator: Beth Behner
Revision Project Coordinator for M6, 5th ed.: Polly Fulton

Library of Congress Cataloging-in-Publication Data

Water meters--selection, installation, testing, and maintenance. -- 5th ed.
p. cm. -- (AWWA manual ; M6)
Includes bibliographical references and index.
ISBN 978-1-58321-862-4
1. Water-meters. I. American Water Works Association.
TD499.W383 2012
628.1'44--dc23

2012004592

Printed in the United States of America
American Water Works Association
6666 West Quincy Avenue
Denver, CO 80235-3098
ISBN 978-1-58321-862-4

Printed on recycled paper

Contents

Figures

Tables

Foreword

This manual is a guide to selecting, installing, testing, and maintaining water meters. The manual discusses recommended practices; it is not an AWWA standard calling for compliance with certain specifications. It is intended for use by new and existing utilities of all sizes, either as a textbook for those not fully familiar with meters or as a reference manual. Water utilities may use this manual as a tool to obtain the best revenue for their investment in meters and maintenance facilities. Design engineers and consultants may use this manual in laying out new meter installations or repair shops.

Most readers will first use this manual for assistance on an individual problem; however, for adequate knowledge of the field of water meter usage, the entire manual should be studied. This manual references applicable AWWA standards for the various types of meters. These standards may be purchased by calling AWWA Customer Service (800.926.7337) or through the Bookstore section of the AWWA website, awwa.org.

The AWWA manual on water meters was first published in a series of articles in the June, July, August, and September 1959 issues of *Journal - American Water Works Association* and was compiled as a separate reprint in 1962. A second edition of the manual was published in 1973, as a complete revision, updating and substantially enlarging the 1962 serial edition. The third and fourth editions, published in 1986 and 1999, respectively, reflected the latest revisions of the AWWA meter standards at the time and included substantial updates to the text and photographs.

This fifth edition contains current information from the latest AWWA meter standards, including new AWWA standards on singlejet meters and fluidic-oscillator meters. Since 1999, much has changed in meter reading technology, and the future holds even greater promise.

Acknowledgments

The AWWA Standards Subcommittee on Revision of Manual M6, which developed this fifth edition, had the following personnel at the time:

Floyd S. Salser Jr., *Chair*

S. Bartram, Elster AMCO Water, Ocala, Fla.
T.D. Bianchi, Neptune Technology Group Inc., Tallassee, Ala.
T. Butler, Itron, Silver Springs, Fla.
M.D. Cole, Infinity Metering Company Inc., Ocala, Fla.
G.H. De Jarlais, Badger Meter Inc., Milwaukee, Wis.
A. Dudley, Itron, Greenwood, S.C.
G. Gomez, Badger Meter Inc., Milwaukee, Wis.
D.E. Hood, M.E. Simpson Company Inc., Valparaiso, Ind.
J.E. Jackson, Sensus Metering Systems, Texarkana, Texas
M.C. Johnson, Utah State University, Logan, Utah
M.J. Kebles, Water Industry Consultant, Las Vegas, Nev.
T.A. Kelly Jr., Washington Suburban Sanitary Commission, Laurel, Md.
R.N. Koch, Master Meter Inc., Pittsburgh, Pa.
D.J. Kullmann, Neptune Technology Group Inc., Marietta, Ga.
G.G. Land, Dallas Water Utilities, Dallas, Texas
R.A. Richter, National Institute of Standards and Technology, Gaithersburg, Md.
F.S. Salser Jr., Floyd S. Salser Jr. & Assoc. d.b.a. MARS Company, Ocala, Fla.
S.H. Seehoffer, Master Meter Inc., Mansfield, Texas
M. Shamley, Metron-Farnier, Boulder, Colo.
S.M. Swanson, Sensus Metering Systems, Uniontown, Pa.
M.A. Thomas, Mueller Systems, Cleveland, N.C.
A.M. Watson, Elster AMCO Water, Ocala, Fla.
J.A. Welsh, Measurement Canada, Ottawa, Ont., Canada

The AWWA Standards Committee on Water Meters, which reviewed and approved this manual, had the following personnel at the time of approval:

Michael J. Kebles, *Chair*
Thomas Gwynn, *Secretary***

General Interest Members

R.C. Graff, Poway, Calif.
D.E. Hood, M.E. Simpson Company Inc., Valparaiso, Ind.
M.C. Johnson, Utah State University, Logan, Utah
M.J. Kebles, Water Industry Consultant, Las Vegas, Nev.
*F.S. Kurtz,** Standards Engineer Liaison, AWWA, Denver, Colo.
R.A. Richter, National Institute of Standards and Technology, Gaithersburg, Md.
F.S. Salser Jr., Floyd S. Salser & Assoc. d.b.a. MARS Company, Ocala, Fla.
R. San Giacomo, R & D Engineering P.C., Orchard Park, N.Y.
J.A. Welsh, Measurement Canada, Ottawa, Ont., Canada

Producer Members

S. Bartram,† Elster AMCO Water, Ocala, Fla.
T.D. Bianchi,† Neptune Technology Group Inc., Tallassee, Ala.
T. Butler, Itron, Silver Springs, Fla.
M.D. Cole, Infinity Metering Company Inc., Ocala, Fla.
G.H. De Jarlais,† Badger Meter Inc., Milwaukee, Wis.
A. Dudley,† Itron, Greenwood, S.C.
L.W. Fleury Jr., Mueller Group, Smithfield, R.I.
G. Gomez, Badger Meter, Milwaukee, Wis.
A. Hendey, Performance Meter, Beaumont, Calif.
R. Howard,† Performance Meter, Banning, Calif.
J.E. Jackson,† Sensus Metering Systems Inc., Texarkana, Texas
M.J. Keilty, Endress+Hauser Flowtec AG, Lyons, Colo.
R.N. Koch, Master Meter Inc., Pittsburgh, Pa.
D.J. Kullmann, Neptune Technology Group Inc., Marietta, Ga.
M. Laird,† Metron-Farnier, Boulder, Colo.
J.F. Panek Jr.,† McCrometer Inc., Rowley, Iowa
J. Potter,† Master Meter, Mansfield, Texas
M. Shamley, Metron-Farnier, Boulder, Colo.
S.M. Swanson, Sensus Metering Systems, Uniontown, Pa.
M.A. Thomas,† Mueller Systems, Cleveland, N.C.
G.M. Voss, McCrometer Inc., Hemet, Calif.
A.M. Watson, Elster AMCO Water, Ocala, Fla.

User Members

M.L. Aigen, Boston Water and Sewer Commission, Roxbury, Mass.
J. Alongi, Kansas City Water Services Department, Kansas City, Mo.
M.J. Aragon, Denver Water, Denver, Colo.
M.C. Bowen, City of Columbus, Division of Water, Columbus, Ohio
W.F. Dunnill, Consolidated Utility District of Rutherford County, Murfreesboro, Tenn.
W.M. Garfield, Arizona Water Company, Phoenix, Ariz.
D. Griffin, City of Winnipeg Water and Waste Dept., Winnipeg, Man., Canada
P.A. Hayes, Glendale Water & Power, Glendale, Calif.
N.D. Kaufman, Truckee Donner Public Utility District, Truckee, Calif.
T.A. Kelly Jr., Washington Suburban Sanitary Commission, Laurel, Md.
M.S. Krause, Desert Water Agency, Palm Springs, Calif.
G.G. Land, Dallas Water Utilities, Dallas, Texas
*S.U. Mills,** Standards Council Liaison, City of Arlington, Arlington, Texas
K.C. Molli, Veolia Water North America, Chicago, Ill.
J.A. Novak, Milwaukee Water Works, Milwaukee, Wis.
G.E. Raymond, Los Angeles Department of Water and Power, Los Angeles, Calif.
S. Solotoff, Miami-Dade Water & Sewer, Miami, Fla.
J.H. Standi Jr., Golden State Water Company, Fontana, Calif.

---

* Liaison, nonvoting
** Nonvoting
† Alternate

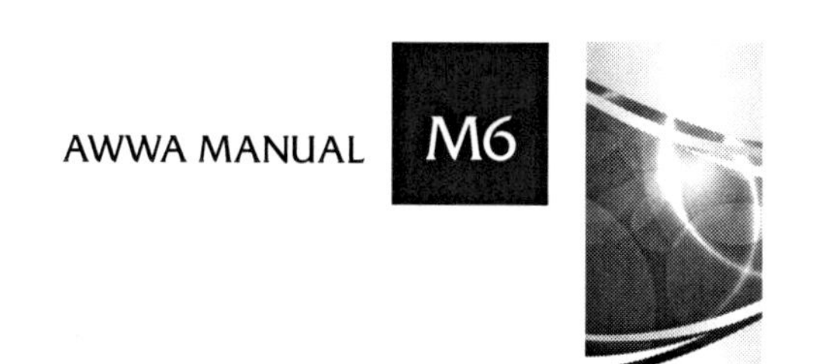

Chapter 1

History of Water Measurement and Development of Water Meters

INTRODUCTION

Accurate water measurement is the means by which water utilities produce revenue to cover expenses, charge each customer equitably, prevent waste of water, and minimize the load on wastewater facilities. This concept is universally accepted today, but it took thousands of years for the science of water supply and distribution to reach its present state.

WATER SUPPLY IN ANCIENT TIMES

Roman Adjutages

For nearly half a century, until 312 B.C.E., the citizens of Rome were content to draw their water supply from the Tiber River, wells, and springs. As in our own times, such sources became entirely inadequate to meet the needs of a rapidly growing city, and the first of the great aqueducts, the Appian, was constructed. This was followed 40 years later by the Anio Vetus and during the next three centuries by seven other aqueducts.

All of these aqueducts are described in meticulous detail by water commissioner Sextus Julius Frontinus (approximately A.D. 35 to 104) in his two books of *De Aquis Urbis Romae* (translated into English by Clemens Herschel under the title *The Water Supply of the City of Rome*).

Chapter 1

History of Water Measurement and Development of Water Meters

INTRODUCTION

Accurate water measurement is the means by which water utilities produce revenue to cover expenses, charge each customer equitably, prevent waste of water, and minimize the load on wastewater facilities. This concept is universally accepted today, but it took thousands of years for the science of water supply and distribution to reach its present state.

WATER SUPPLY IN ANCIENT TIMES

Roman Adjutages

For nearly half a century, until 312 B.C.E., the citizens of Rome were content to draw their water supply from the Tiber River, wells, and springs. As in our own times, such sources became entirely inadequate to meet the needs of a rapidly growing city, and the first of the great aqueducts, the Appian, was constructed. This was followed 40 years later by the Anio Vetus and during the next three centuries by seven other aqueducts.

All of these aqueducts are described in meticulous detail by water commissioner Sextus Julius Frontinus (approximately A.D. 35 to 104) in his two books of *De Aquis Urbis Romae* (translated into English by Clemens Herschel under the title *The Water Supply of the City of Rome*).

The contributions made by Frontinus cannot be overstated. The office of water commissioner was held, from ancient times, by the most distinguished citizens. Frontinus set an example for all future water commissioners to follow in his honest devotion to duty, thoroughness of accomplishment, and sterling character. Those who read his voluminous report today can still profit and are astonished over the progress made during those ancient times in the development of metal pipe, pipe fittings, plug cocks, inverted siphons, ornate fountains and baths, and possibly in methods of measurement and filtration. Herschel comments:

> It must be remembered that we are speaking of the works of a very practical people. They were engineers by nature, rather than architects or men of science only; they taught the useful from choice, rather than that which was merely beautiful in design or tendency. They felt comparatively little predilection for "pursuing science for science's sake," as the phrase goes, while they pursued to the utmost of their abilities, and most ably for their day, the "art of directing the great sources of power in nature for the use and convenience of man," which constitutes the profession of the civil engineer.

After describing in great detail the construction of the nine huge aqueducts, Frontinus wrote:

> Having now given the builders and the age of each aqueduct, also their sources, lengths of channel, and order of heights, it seems to me not out of keeping to go more into detail, and to demonstrate how large is the quantity of water which is allotted to public and to private uses, as well as for luxury; and through how many tanks it is conveyed, and in what wards these are located; *how much water* is distributed within the city walls, how much without, how much is used for water basins, how much for fountains, how much for public structures, how much on account of the state, how much by private consumers. But before I mention the names *quinaria, centenaria*, and those of the other adjutages (Figure 1-1) by which water is gaged, I deem it expedient to state what is their origin, what their discharge, capacity, or value, and what each name means; and to show, after presenting the rules according to which their proportions and capacity are computed, how I discovered their discrepancies, and the way I set about to correct them.
>
> The adjutages to measure water are arranged either according to digits or inches. Digits are used down to the present day in Campania, and in very many places in Italy; inches in Apulia and elsewhere. The digit, according to common agreement, is the one sixteenth part of a foot, the inch the twelfth; but even as there is a difference between the inch and digit, so also digits differ among themselves; some are called square, others round. The square digit is greater than the round digit by three fourteenths of itself; the round digit is smaller than the square digit by three elevenths, obviously because the corners are lopped off.

Just a few paragraphs further, we find the amazing statement:

> But every adjutage is gaged either by its diameter or circumference, or by its area of clear cross section; from any of which its capacity may be found.

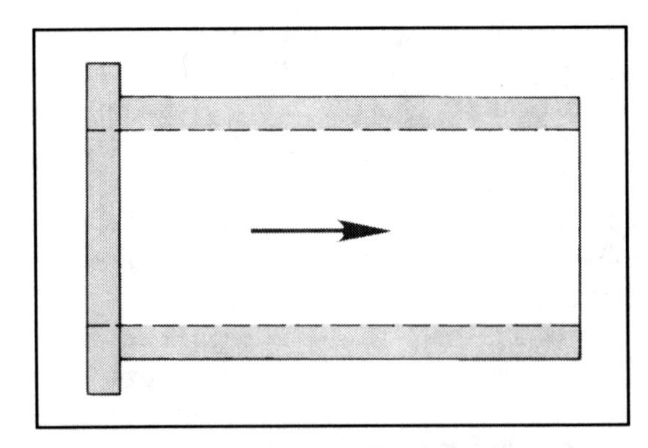

An adjutage was a simple bronze tube of a specific cross section. No precise means for measuring the velocity of water passing through the tube was available.

Figure 1-1 Roman adjutage

It seems natural that we turn to Herschel for pointed comment. He writes:

> Let us see what ideas were extant on hydraulics in Frontinus' time: The most troublesome point of ignorance he had to contend with was a total inability to measure the velocity of water, or even to rightly and fully grasp the idea of such velocity, whether as flowing in an open channel or in closed pipes. He accordingly compares streams of water merely by the areas of their cross sections. A square foot of water is all one to him, whether it be one of the 8 sq ft (0.7 m^2) of cross-sectional area of a stream in a conduit, or whether it be composed of the sum of 200 or more cross-sectional areas of lead pipes leading out of delivery tanks to fountains, or to water basins, or to private consumers, and ending and discharging at as many different elevations. To the expert of today, this seems excessively silly; and yet the same thing is constantly being done even now by those who ought to know better. The average man today will talk about "a stream of water that will fill a 6-in. (150-mm) pipe," a perfect parallel to the *quinaric* (0.907 English inch) of Frontinus; and there are hundreds of deeds on record conveying "square feet of water" for power purposes, just as though the law of falling bodies and its application to hydraulics had never been discovered; and unmindful of the fact, as one old Italian writer on water rights has expressed it, that to speak of a stream of water by its area of cross section is like estimating the volume of a cylinder merely from the area of its base.

Yet at least some evidence suggests, as we read Frontinus, that he was frequently troubled over his adoption of pipe area as the sole measure of volume discharge, because at one point in his history he wrote:

> Let us not forget in this connection that every stream of water whenever it comes from a higher point and flows into a delivery tank through a short length of pipe, not only comes up to its measure, but yields, moreover, a surplus; but whenever it comes from a low point, that is, under a less(er) head, and is conducted a tolerably long distance it will actually shrink in measure by the resistance of its own conduit so that, on these accounts, either an aid or a check is needed for the discharge.

In other words, a check of some sort was required *to make the pipe discharge the quantity typical for its size*. Frontinus continues:

> . . . whence it appears that the amount measured by me is none too large; the explanation of this is that the more impetuous stream of water increases the supply, since it comes from a large and rapidly flowing river.

Herschel comments:

> And then he goes on again, worrying himself into all sorts of explanations why his gagings by areas, made irrespective of heads and velocities, do not balance. The frauds of the watermen, of the plumbers, and of others who draw water unlawfully always furnish a handy explanation, however.

We become increasingly perplexed when we realize that Hero of Alexandria, thought by some to be the teacher of Frontinus, had already announced:

> Observe always that it does not suffice to determine the section of flow, to know the quantity of water furnished by the spring. This we said was 12 square digits. It is necessary to find the velocity of its current, because the more rapid the flow, the more water the spring will furnish, and the slower it is, the less it will produce. For this reason, after having dug a reservoir under the stream, examine by means of a Sundial how much water flows into it in an hour, and from that deduce the quantity of water furnished in a day. Thus one has no need to measure the section of the stream.

Notwithstanding the false premise of Frontinus, here indeed was the beginning of the art of measuring flowing water, which will be emphasized as we continue on to further developments in Roman practice.

Quoting Herschel:

> But some control of the amount drawn had to exist, and we accordingly find that the measure of a grant in the city of Rome, A.D. 97, was the right to insert, at a designated place in the public delivery tanks, or cisterns, which received their supply, either directly or through lead pipes, from the public aqueducts, a circular bronze adjutage, or short piece of pipe, stamped by the public authority, not less than about nine inches long and of a designated diameter, some fifteen such diameters being in ordinary use; and to allow water naturally to flow through this adjutage; it being the law, moreover, to ensure a natural flow through the stamped bronze adjutage, that the lead or other pipe immediately downstream from it should have the same diameter as the adjutage, on a length of not less than 50 ft (15 m), measuring from the downstream end of the adjutage.

Frontinus definitely realized that there were other factors limiting the quantity of water that could be drawn. He wrote:

> An adjutage placed at right angles and level, it maintains its proper measure; set against the current of the water and sloping down, it will consume more; set sloping to one side, so that the water flows by, and inclined with the current, that is, placed less favorably for swallowing water, it will receive the water slowly, and in a scant quantity.
>
> It must also be left optional to attach any kind of lead pipe to the adjutages; but there must rather be attached for a length of 50 ft (15 m) one of the same interior area as that which the adjutage has been certified to have, as has been ordinated by a vote of the Senate that "no one to whom a right to draw water from the public conduits has been granted shall have the

right to use a larger pipe than a *quinaria* for a space of 50 ft (15 m) from the delivery tank out of which he is to draw the water."

The water commissioner called attention to fraud that was being practiced by attaching pipes of larger diameter to the adjutages and, as a consequence, the water was not, he said, "held together for the lawful distance."

The Naples Museum exhibits three small bronze pipes believed to be genuine adjutages 9-in. (230-mm) long and 0.72 in. (18 mm) in diameter. It was required that

- The adjutage be entered at a designated point
- Water rights limited the quantity of water to be drawn and ended with the death of the grantee
- The setting of the orifices be determined by the authorities
- Adjutages be of a prescribed form, dimension, and material (bronze), and bear the official stamp of the authorities

Frontinus reports "cheating practices" discovered, in addition to the larger outlet pipe mentioned, as follows:

> To some pipes no adjutages were attached. Such pipes are called uncontrolled, and are expanded or contracted as pleases the watermen.
>
> When a water right is transferred to a new owner they will insert a new adjutage in the delivery tank; the old one they leave in the tank and draw water from it, which they sell.

He adds significantly: "Most especially, therefore, as I believe, should the commissioner have in mind to stop this."

MEASURING DEVICES OF MORE RECENT TIMES

The remainder of this chapter discusses more recent developments in devices for measuring water and their acceptance by water utilities. In addition, standardization issues are discussed.

The Pitot Tube

In 1730, Henri Pitot (1695–1771), a distinguished French engineer, performed experiments on the river Seine in which he used a vertical glass tube with the short, 90° tip at the lower end pointing upstream to determine whether there was a relationship between the rise of water in the tube and the velocity of flow (Figure 1-2). Two years later, he contributed a paper to l'Academie Royale des Sciences describing his experiments and his tube, which he had combined with a second, static-head vertical tube. Significantly, his discovery that the height to which the water rose in his tube was proportional to the square of the stream velocity came in the same year that Johann Bernoulli published the fundamental relationship of head to velocity squared of water flowing through pipes.

One hundred and twenty-five years later, Henry Darcy, another French engineer, modified the tube and thus improved the accuracy of the static-head readings and reduced the oscillations of the water columns. Hiram F. Mills of Boston was the first American engineer to use the Pitot tube (1875); John R. Freeman applied the Pitot tube to the measurement of fire-stream jets. The design illustrated in Figure 1-3 is used primarily for this purpose.

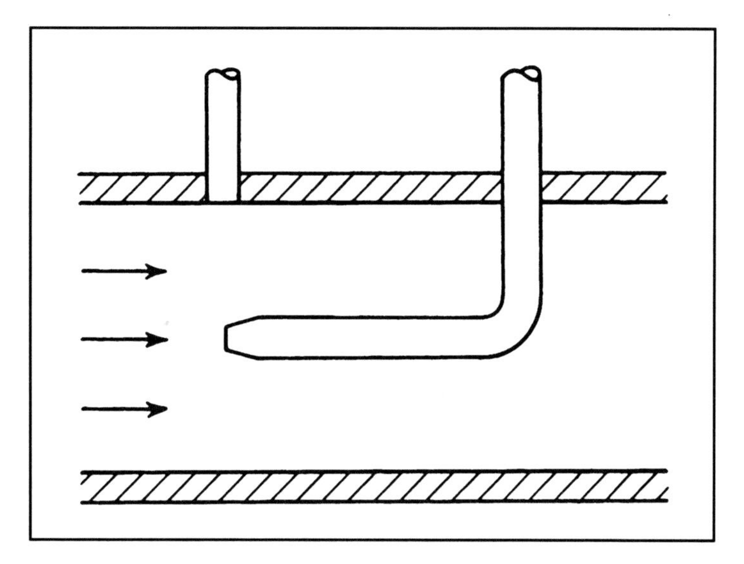

The Pitot tube measures the velocity of the flowing fluid by using the velocity head of the stream as an index of velocity.

Figure 1-2 Pitot tube

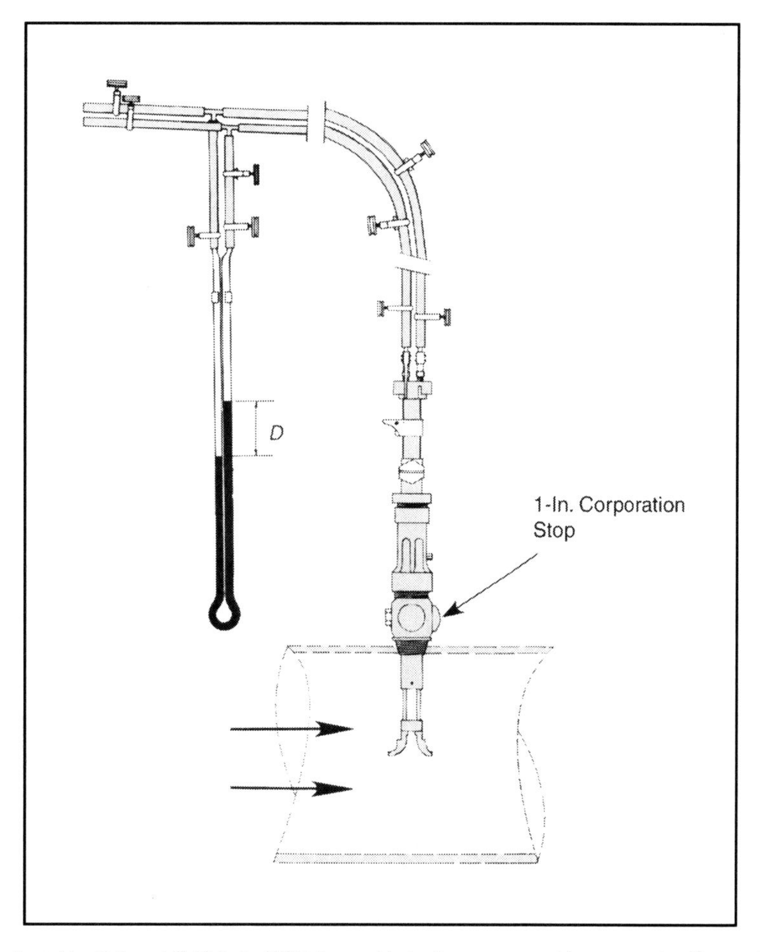

This form of Pitot tube, designed by Edward S. Cole in 1896, is used in leak surveys and for measuring flow and pipeline capacity.

Figure 1-3 Modified Pitot tube

Today, the temporary measurement of the rate of flow in a large pipe is sometimes necessary, for example, to locate underground leaks or determine variations in flow rates over a 24-hour period. The type of Pitot tube commonly used for these applications (Figure 1-3), developed by Edward S. Cole in 1896, requires a single, very basic connection into the pipeline. This modified Pitot tube depends on the velocity of the flowing water creating flowing pressure greater than the line pressure in the tube pointed upstream and reduction below the line pressure in a similar tube pointed downstream, both located in the center of the pipe. This differential is mathematically converted into a gallons-per-minute flow rate when the internal diameter of the pipe is known.

Current and Turbine Meters

In 1790, Benjamin G. Hoffman, in Hamburg, Germany, published a booklet describing a form of current meter, invented by Reinhard Woltmann (1757–1837), for measuring flowing air and water. This device seems to be the first practical meter for the purpose; it has since changed materially in design and construction.

In general, the meter consisted of a very light waterwheel operated by the current and carrying on its axis a worm for actuating gearing and a totalizer. The rate of flow was computed from the rotations during a given time period. A 1910 American Society of Mechanical Engineers (ASME) paper, entitled "River Discharge," refers to the earliest type of current meter as being practical only for measuring surface velocity. However, the ASME paper noted, "About 1790, Woltmann modified this wheel so it could be used beneath the surface" (Figures 1-4, 1-5, and 1-6). Each size of meter had to be calibrated individually.

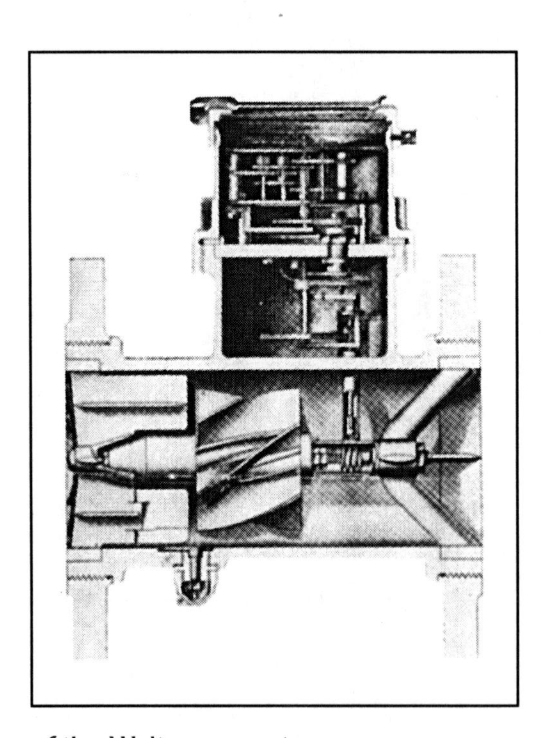

Figure 1-4 Improved form of the Woltmann meter

Figure 1-5 Cutaway of an "open or interchangeable" internal mechanism Woltmann-type turbine meter

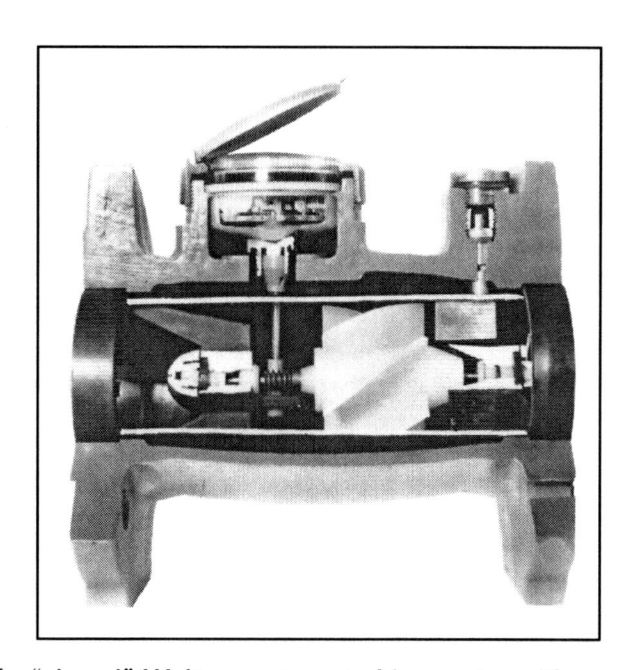

Figure 1-6 Cutaway of a "closed" Woltmann-type turbine meter with magnetic drive

The Woltmann meter (Figure 1-7) was illustrated and described in a German handbook, *Die Hydraulik Und Die Hydraulischen Motoren*, by Georg Meissner, published in Jena, Germany, in 1878. At that time, it was not generally accepted that the meter could be used in a closed pipe. The first English water meter was designed in 1851, by William Siemens (1823–1883). Siemens obtained permission to manufacture this reaction meter in Germany, and the firm of Siemens & Halske began production about 1865. Although such meters appeared to give fairly accurate results, the hydraulic laws governing their action were never fully understood, and the designs were therefore empirical. Corrosion caused considerable trouble because the meter casings were made of cast iron and the internal working parts of bronze.

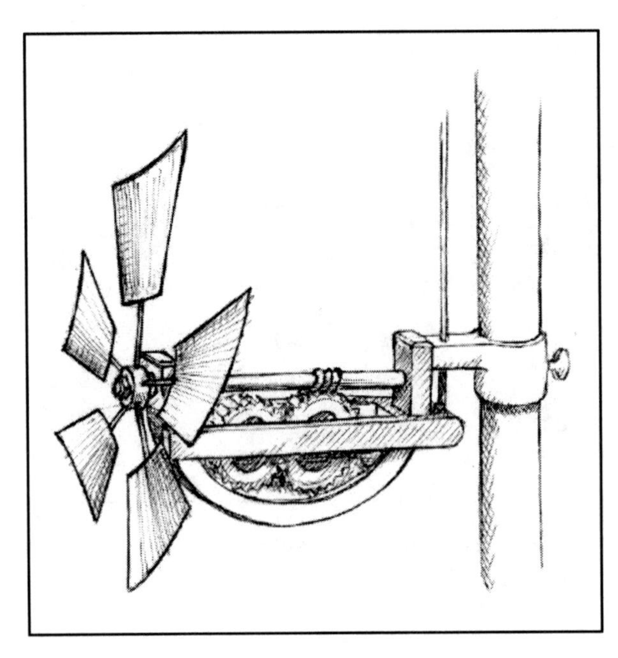

In this form, the Woltmann meter could measure flows only in an open stream. The revolutions of the waterwheel were transmitted to a register by a gear train. For a stream of known cross section, the register could be calibrated to give accurate measurements of flow.

Figure 1-7 Original form of the Woltmann meter

In 1885, Ross E. Browne, in his book *Water Meters*, described the English Siemens ½-in. (13-mm) meter, which somewhat resembled a centrifugal pump reversed, using a drum reaction wheel controlled by regulating vanes. The German Siemens was an early form of the rotary-vane meter. Water entered the measuring chamber through angularly positioned inlets, causing the flow to impinge on one side of the vanes of the rotor at a 90° angle. To prevent the rotor from spinning too fast, other, much smaller inlets entered the chamber at an opposite angle, creating a small force in the other direction. This meter was substantially different from the conventional turbine meter in which the water strikes the blades of a rotor at approximately 45°. Today many small rotary-vane meters are manufactured outside the United States.

Whereas the Woltmann meter had a horizontal axis that permitted a straight-through flow, the current or turbine meters developed in the United States since 1890 and until the 1960s usually had a vertical rotor spindle. This design facilitated a vertical drive to the register, but necessitated changes in flow direction within the meter to keep the inlet and outlet in a straight line (Figure 1-8).

With the advent of magnetic drives, some models have returned to the horizontal rotor spindle, which gives lower pressure loss. The first of the modern turbine meters, now referred to as class II turbine meters, was introduced to the market in 1965. Horizontal shaft class I turbines were manufactured for a short time before and during the introduction of horizontal shaft class II turbines. One leading US manufacturer shipped its first unit, called a Torrent meter, in 1896. Its design was later refined to be similar to present construction in Patent 817,887, issued to J.A. Tilden in 1906.

The new class II turbine meter was capable of operating over a much wider flow range than earlier turbine meters, which have been offered by manufacturers since the 1920s. The new horizontal in-line, high-velocity turbine meters are constructed of more modern materials. The new materials for bearings, coupled with low-mass, self-lubricating, low-friction gearing in the registers and gear trains, permit the back loading on the metering elements to be reduced, thus providing improved metering accuracy, range sensitivity, and longevity for this meter.

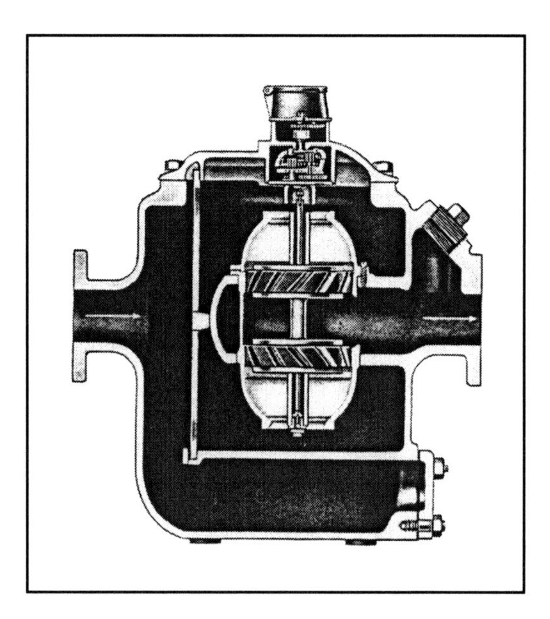

Figure 1-8 Class I turbine meter

The introduction of this newer turbine meter resulted in changes to ANSI/AWWA C701, Standard for Cold Water Meters—Turbine Type, for Customer Service, in 1978. The changes include a newly added distinction between class I and class II turbine meters. Standards for original class I turbines (Figure 1-8) were issued prior to 1978. Class II turbine meters are the newer, in-line, high-velocity type characterized by lower head loss, greater low-flow sensitivity, and tighter accuracy tolerances over a wider flow range (Figure 1-9). The class II turbine meters are considerably smaller and lighter than the class I turbines and afford easier installation as well as smaller accommodations for meter settings. Manufacturers of the class II turbine meters recommend that plate-type strainers be used in the installation upstream from the meter to protect the high-velocity rotors in operation and to decrease the effects of upstream flow disturbances, which affect life and accuracy. Standards for cold-water turbine meters are covered in ANSI/AWWA C701.

In the 1980s, a new version of class I turbine meters was introduced that was similar in size and weight to class II turbine meters. This new class I turbine meter had an internal strainer and a vertical rotor, and thus could be installed in smaller accommodations than many class II turbine meters, which generally require a strainer before the meter.

The Venturi Meter

A major contribution to the measurement of flowing water under pressure was Clemens Herschel's invention of the Venturi tube in 1886. A hydraulic engineer with the Holyoke (Mass.) Water Power Company, he was disturbed by the fact that huge quantities of water used by industrial companies, including 25 paper mills, went unmeasured. The tube was based on the principle, discovered a century earlier by the Italian scientist Giovanni Venturi (1746–1822), that the flow of liquid through a converging pipe results in a gain of velocity and a lowering of pressure, whereas the reverse is true in a diverging pipe. The reduction in pressure that occurs at the constriction is actually the result of conversion of pressure head to velocity head. Downstream from the constriction, the velocity head is reconverted to pressure head, so the ultimate result is very little reduction in effective line pressure at some distance downstream.

Courtesy: Badger Meter Inc.

Figure 1-9 Class II turbine meter. Note the test port on top used for pressure testing, air bleeding, and qualitative low-flow tests.

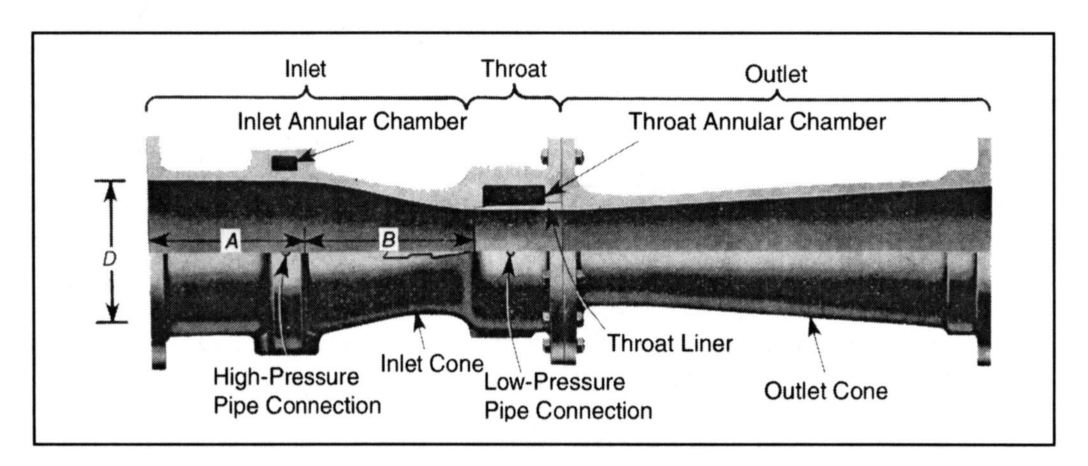

The flow of liquid through a constriction in a pressure conduit results in a lowering of pressure at the constriction. The difference in pressure at the constriction and in the unconstricted portion of the conduit is a function of the flow rate and may be used to calculate the flow rate. The meter has no moving parts in the liquid because it measures pressure differential by means of exterior pressure instruments.

Figure 1-10 Venturi tube

The difference between the full-pressure upstream taps (shown at the left of the constriction in Figure 1-10) and the reduced-pressure taps at the constriction or throat or nozzle (shown in the center of Figure 1-10) is a function of the flow rate and may be used to calculate the flow rate.

The Venturi meter has no moving parts in the stream and is suitable for nearly any size pipeline. One disadvantage of this meter is its length, which makes it bulky and heavy. Recently, however, shorter forms of the Venturi meter, known as flow tubes and flow nozzles, have been developed. These designs have a more abrupt constriction and enlargement. Also, the pressure taps are located differently, which greatly reduces overall length and weight.

One form of mechanical readout is a pressure-actuated pen arm moving across a graduated scale to indicate flow rate or across a moving chart to record the flow rate. More modern versions of the chart recorder are electronic. An integrating attachment may be added that multiplies the pressure differential times time, and then multiplies that result times a constant or coefficient for the particular size of Venturi to register total flow within commercial tolerances.

The Orifice Meter

The orifice meter is considered to be one of the oldest devices for measuring or regulating the flow of fluids, dating back to Caesar's Rome. However, development of the thin-plate orifice, the current standard type, did not begin until the early part of the 20th century.

The determination of the relationship between flow rates and differential pressures has been reduced to formulas by which an orifice coefficient can be computed quickly for any size of orifice in any size of pipe.

Modern differential pressure measurement instruments have an electronic output for recording instruments and incorporate electronic microprocessors for calibrated integration of the differential input signal from the meter. The electrical output signal is linear versus flow rate for flow indicators and data loggers.

The orifice sensing unit consists of a round plate with a hole of predetermined size bored in it, usually concentrically; the plate is inserted across a straight run of pipe. Pressure taps are provided either at specified distances upstream and downstream from the orifice plate or within orifice flanges by which the orifice plate is inserted in the line (Figure 1-11).

This meter is mounted directly above a pipeline. The manometer is not shown because it is located behind the two-pen recorder. If a mercury manometer is used in measuring water or steam, seal pots must be placed in the pressure lines to the manometer.

Figure 1-11 Orifice meter and differential pressure sensing mercury manometer instrument

The ASME publication *Fluid Meters* (4th ed.) explained the characteristics of thin-plate orifices:

> The pressure of the fluid drops abruptly as it flows through the orifice and, on the outlet side, the pressure continues to decrease slightly. The minimum value is reached a short distance from the outlet side of the orifice. Beyond this minimum point, the pressure increases again, slowly at first, then rapidly for a short distance, then again more slowly until its second maximum is reached several pipe diameters beyond the orifice plate. Since no guiding of the stream occurs on either the inlet or the outlet side of an orifice, the acceleration and deceleration of the fluid stream, which the pressure gradient manifests, is accompanied by considerable turbulence and consequent dissipation of energy (pressure), especially on the outlet side. Consequently, for the same diameter ratio, the downstream maximum pressure is much lower for an orifice than it is for a flow nozzle. In other words, the percentage of differential pressure recovered with an orifice is slightly less than with a nozzle and much less than with a Venturi.

The pressure differential created by the orifice is converted into linear motion of a pen arm, or integrator cam, by a manometer, which may be either a mercury or a sealed-bellows type. By calculating the orifice coefficient and drilling the orifice bore to the diameter required, the chart indicator, scale indicator, or integrator can be read in gallons or other units. This procedure is essentially the same whether a Venturi, an orifice, or some other pressure differential meter is used.

Orifice meters are used where space for the sensing unit is too limited for a Venturi meter and where slightly greater pressure loss can be permitted. The range of flow for maximum accuracy is about 3½ to 1. The sensing unit is relatively inexpensive. Orifice meters are widely used in industrial plants for water, steam, and gas, and by gas utilities.

One water-utility application is to measure the flow of water from pumped wells being tested for flow rates. This operation is feasible provided that (1) the pressure differential between the upstream and downstream taps is not more than the limit of the bellows manometer (maximum limit approximately 14 psi [100 kPa]); (2) the orifice plate and flanges fit the pipe correctly; and (3) the discharge leading to the atmosphere can be kept under slight back pressure.

Displacement Meters

The most popular types of displacement meters originated as modifications of pumps that were run backward. Instead of using the mechanism as a prime mover, the water under pressure moved the piston or disc. The number of strokes or the measured volume per cycle was converted into gallons, cubic feet, or other unit of measurement by appropriate gearing.

Although patents for liquid meters were issued earlier, it is believed that the first American water meter was proposed in 1850 by William Sewell of Williamsburg, N.Y. The first meter actually produced is claimed to have been made by Henry R. Worthington of New York (Figure 1-12). At about the same time (1850s), the George Kent Scientific & Mechanical Group of Luton, England, manufactured a duplex-piston meter of nearly identical design. Samples of this meter exist in several European museums and in displays in Chicago and Baltimore meter shops.

These early meters were of reciprocating piston design, patterned after the familiar D-slide valve used in steam engines. Worthington's original meter consisted of two cylinders and plungers with inlet and outlet ports arranged in such a way that as water in one cylinder was discharged by the piston, the other cylinder was filling. Water flow through these meters was subject to pulsations caused by the action of the pistons, and high friction losses were encountered. An analysis of the ⅝-in. (15-mm) Worthington meter, made in 1885 by Ross E. Browne, describes it as having a capacity of 7½ gpm (1.7 m^3/h), weighing 59 lb (27 kg), and costing $17.00.

Close accuracy was impossible because the meter counted the number of piston strokes, whose length varied with the flow rate. Variations in velocity of the strokes caused variable compression of the rubber cushions at each end of the cylinders.

In 1876, a patent was issued for a meter with two rotary pistons. A design for only one piston followed around 1880 (Figure 1-13). The piston rotated within a toothed, fixed cylinder called a crown. In 1885, this design was manufactured in France as the Nasch Crown meter and was also sold in the United States.

Browne also described a single-piston, double-acting meter, the Kennedy. In 1885, it weighed 162 lb (73 kg) in the ½-in. (13-mm) size and sold for $27.83. It measured the travel distance of the piston.

Invented in the 1850s, this was the first practical meter produced in the United States.

Figure 1-12 Original duplex-piston meter

Although an improvement over the two-piston design, this type of meter was subject to high friction losses.

Figure 1-13 Early rotary-piston meter

Between 1870 and 1910, more than 400 patents were issued on liquid meters. Many of these patents described constructions that were hopelessly impractical and complicated; others protected any possible variation of valuable features. One of these patents (114,694), issued to J.P. Lindsay in 1871, described an oscillating disc meter, which today would be called a reciprocating meter with a single piston. This meter was round and flat in shape and controlled by a reversing valve. Most of these early designs had impractical features, such as the use of moving valves; the need for some parts to start and stop during each cycle of measurement; the use of floats, of back-and-forth oscillating motion of the piston, and of the inner face of the housing as the measuring chamber; the inlet and outlet not on a common axis centered in the meter; inadequate capacity resulting in excessive pressure loss; and apparently no consideration for manufacturing costs.

Also, these meters, although purporting to be displacement meters, were only semipositive. The high friction load and complex moving parts must have permitted much slippage, thus impairing low-flow accuracy. Present displacement meters have capillary seals rather than packing seals to prevent slippage, but, in any event, the excellence of manufacture reduces slippage to a negligible factor.

In 1884, the first practical oscillating-piston meter patent was issued to Lewis H. Nash. He stated in his patent that this meter was an adaptation of an existing steam engine, but the piston shape and movement are similar to the oscillating-piston meters of today. It was a simple, workable measuring unit.

The nutating-piston principle of motion (now the disc meter) is reported to have been invented in the 1830s by an English clergyman and used in a steam engine. During the 1840s, it was an accepted type of engine, and the presses of the London *Times* were run by this type of engine. However, it was not an efficient prime mover because of the lack of sufficiently tight packing around the edge of the disc portion of the piston; thus it fell into disuse.

A nutating-piston liquid pump, using what today would be called a conical disc, was patented in the United States in 1854 by D.S. Carpenter (Patent 11,776). A modification, also for use as a pump, was patented by Charles H. Hersey in 1868.

The date of the first nutating-piston or disc meter is not clear. Limited patents on this type were issued in 1887 and 1888, and Patent 486,992, issued in 1892 to J.A. Tilden, covered features of a flat-disc meter. In that same year, two companies that are still in the meter business today were organized, one to manufacture conical-disc meters and the other flat-disc meters. A third company was already making conical-disc meters.

All these manufacturers had problems with hard rubber discs breaking at fast flows. One solution, developed by John Thomson in his Patents 476,102; 485,437 (1892); and 535,641 (1895); was for a thrust roller to control the circumferential thrust of the disc in its movement and thus prevent jamming of the disc against the diaphragm at the slot. This method continues to be widely used.

Another approach was to mold a metal reinforcement into the hard rubber disc section of the nutating piston. The diaphragm was then used as a thrust plate to prevent rotation. In all these designs, the disc section (whether flat or conical) was made as thin as possible to reduce weight; however, this necessitated a very close fit between the edge of the disc and the chamber wall to minimize slippage. In 1892, G.B. Bassett designed and began manufacturing ⅝-in. (15-mm) conical-disc meters with the disc section ¼-in. (6-mm) thick, instead of 3⁄32 in. (2 mm) or less. He found the added weight to be no apparent disadvantage, but the greater thickness gave a more perfect capillary seal against slippage for a given clearance. A reinforcing plate was later added.

The early use of meters was largely in the north, where freezing troubles were frequent. In cold weather, many homeowners drained water pipes at night. The conical-disc meter was favored at this time, because it could be drained more readily than the flat-disc type. To prevent frost damage when pipes were not drained, two features were developed. John Thomson's Patent 520,197 of 1894 covered a breakable frost bottom to be "blown out by the expansive action of freezing." His Patent 771,337 of 1904 covered the use of bolts that would "break, strip or yield resiliently" under pressure greater than normal but yet within the strength of the casings.

Protection of the reducing gear train against wear by enclosing the gears in a grease-filled chamber came into widespread use following World War I. The grease-filled chamber was actually a very old device. The French Nasch meter of 1885 had this feature, as did the English Siemens. Other early patents implied it, without claiming the chamber as invention. The oil-enclosed gear train remained standard until the advent of magnetic-drive meters between 1958 and 1960.

New magnetic materials that retained a high magnetic power indefinitely and were inexpensive were developed, which led to a major change in small-meter design. In the late 1950s, the magnetic drive was developed by several companies, most of which used small four-pole, and later two-pole, usually round, ceramic magnets. (Details are described in chapter 6.) The use of these magnets eliminated the stuffing box and gear train, transmitting the motion through the top of the bronze casing by magnetic flux. By 1970, almost all small meters built in the United States and many large ones were of this design (Figures 1-14, 1-15, and 1-16.) Present standards for displacement meters are ANSI/AWWA C700, Standard for Cold-Water Meters—Displacement Type, Bronze Main Case; and ANSI/AWWA C710, Standard for Cold-Water Meters—Displacement Type, Plastic Main Case.

Multijet Meters

Multijet meters were first designed and produced in Germany beginning with Siemens & Halske in 1867. At least one US meter manufacturer marketed a multijet meter in the late 1920s and into the 1930s for export, primarily to Latin American countries. They have been available to the US water industry since the early 1960s.

Multijet meters are manufactured in two basic designs, classified as wet- and dry-register models (see Figures 1-17 and 1-18.) The introduction of magnetic drives for meters has made the dry-register meter more prevalent. The multijet meter uses the inferential measuring element principle.

Tangential openings in the chamber direct the water flow across a multivaned rotor. The output speed of the rotor is proportional to the quantity of water passing through the measuring chamber.

This meter has a permanently sealed register unit with no changeable calibrating gears.

Figure 1-14 Displacement-type oscillating-piston meter with magnetic drive

This meter has a seated register unit that can be opened for repairs and uses calibrating gears (frost-bottom model shown).

Figure 1-15 Displacement-type nutating-disc meter with magnetic drive

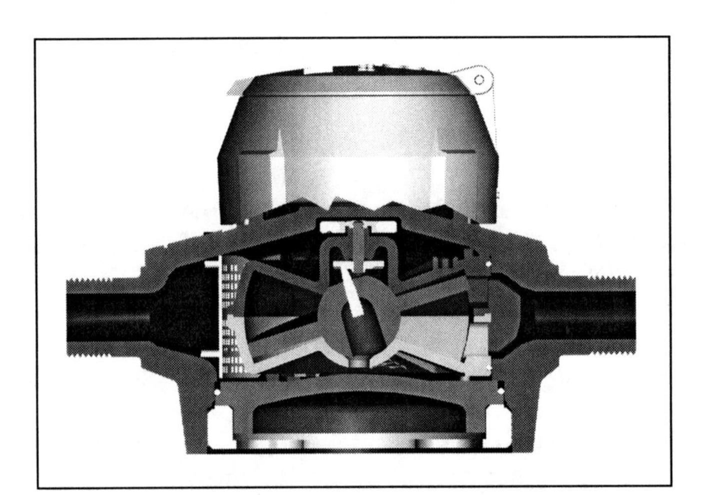

Courtesy: Badger Meter Inc.

Figure 1-16 AWWA standard C710 positive displacement meter, nutating-meter type

Multijet meters with remote registration are also available. Some remote-register systems use a battery-powered unit for operation, while others have been modified to accept modern encoded registers and automatic meter reading (AMR) systems. The operating characteristics for multijet meters are covered in ANSI/AWWA C708, Standard for Cold-Water Meters—Multijet Type, which was introduced in 1976.

Fluidic-Oscillator Meters

In these meters, water enters the fluidic oscillator through a nozzle that forms an accelerated jet. When the jet enters the flow chamber, it initially is drawn to one of the two diffuser walls. The jet travels along the wall and exits the flow chamber. A small portion of the flow migrates through the feedback channel and impinges on the incoming jet. This causes the jet to flip to the other side of the chamber, where the process is repeated. This principle is known as the Coanda effect. The oscillation between the

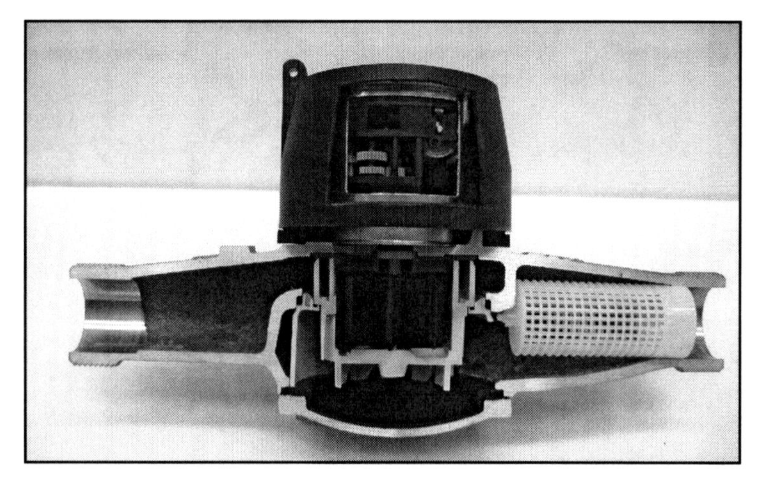

Courtesy: Elster AMCO Water Inc.

Figure 1-17 Cutaway of a dry-head multijet meter without a "frost protection" device

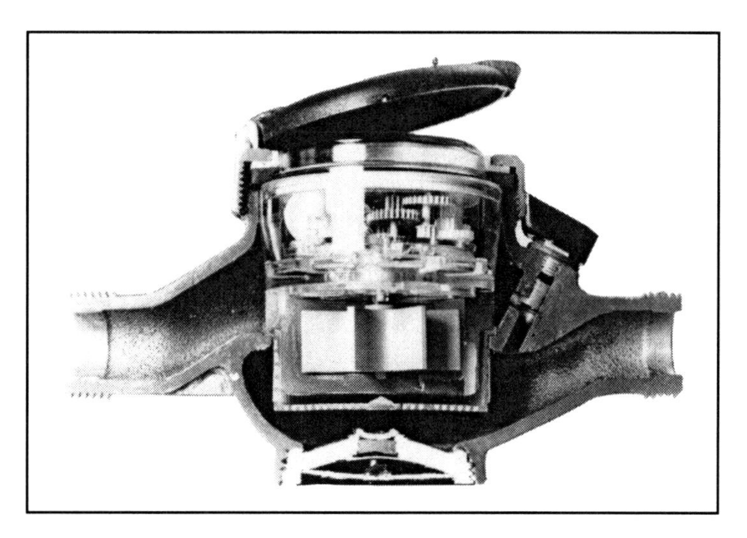

Figure 1-18 Cutaway of a dry-head multijet meter with a patented "frost protection" device

diffuser walls is continuous while flow is present, with the frequency of oscillation proportional to the volume of water moved through the chamber. The oscillation is sensed by electrodes placed next to each diffuser wall. An electrical current is induced in the jet from which the rate of oscillation is calculated and, over a period of time, a total flow is derived.

Figures 1-19 and 1-20 illustrate the fluidic oscillator internal mechanism.

The standard for fluidic-oscillator meters is ANSI/AWWA C713, Cold Water Meters—Fluidic Oscillator Type.

Singlejet Meters

Singlejet water meters were initially developed in Europe in the early 1900s. Singlejet meters have been widely manufactured and used worldwide since that time but were not introduced into the North American market until the early 1990s.

A singlejet meter is a velocity-type meter that incorporates a "single" tangential jet. A tapered or full-size throat targets the water stream across a vertical shaft

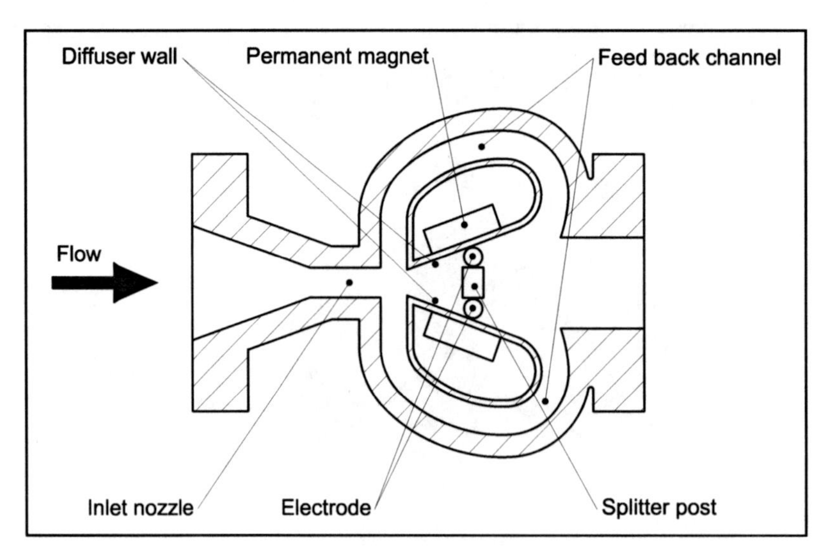

Courtesy: Elster AMCO Water Inc.

Figure 1-19 A section view of the fluidic oscillator internal mechanism

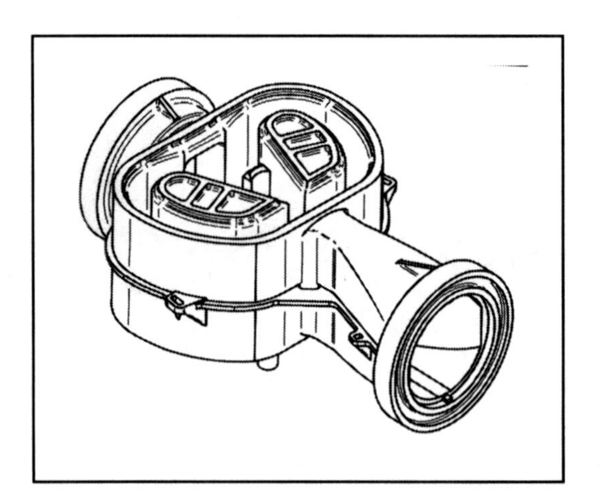

Courtesy: Elster AMCO Water Inc.

Figure 1-20 An isometric view of the fluidic oscillator internal mechanism

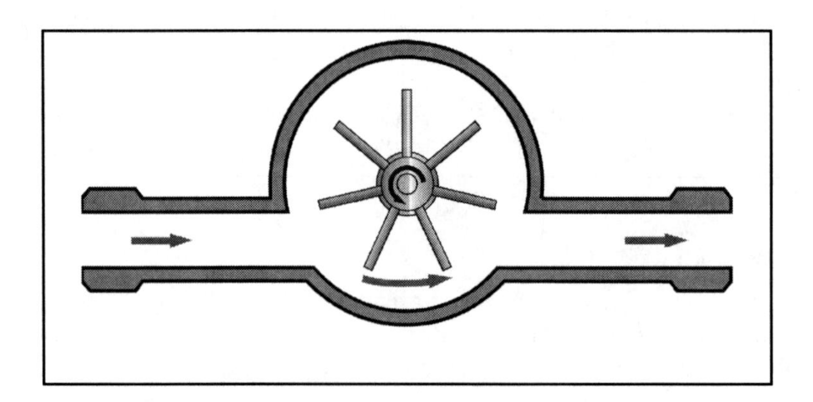

Courtesy: Itron

Figure 1-21 Simplified drawing of the singlejet meter

impeller. The impeller is offset from the water flowing through the tangential jet such that the water travels perpendicular to the rotational axis of the impeller. This is the characteristic that separates the singlejet meter from a typical turbine meter, where water flows along the rotational axis rather than perpendicular to it. By operating perpendicular to the impeller, water flow through the singlejet meter exerts very little force on the bearings.

Figures 1-21 to 1-23 provide illustrations of singlejet meters.

The standard for singlejet meters is ANSI/AWWA C712, Cold Water Meters—Singlejet Type.

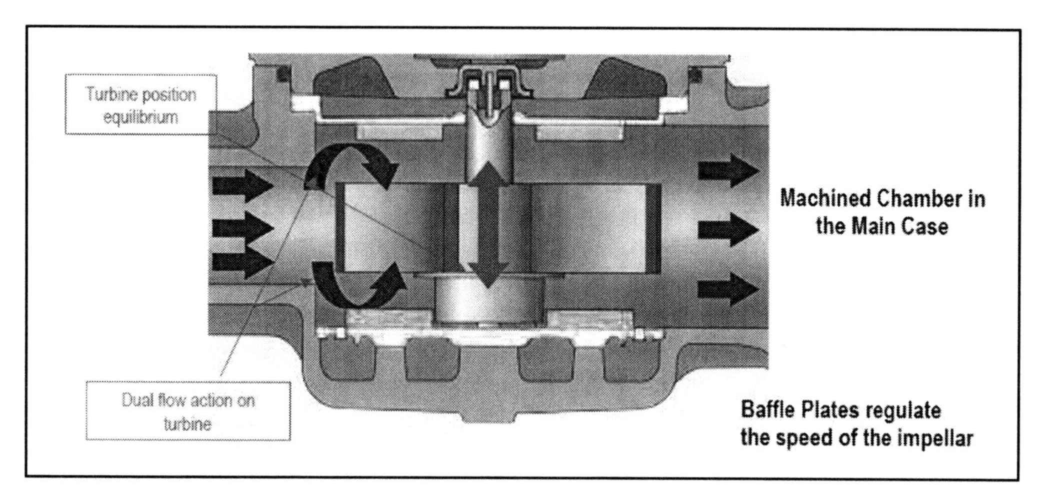

Courtesy: Itron

Figure 1-22 Design details of the singlejet meter

Courtesy: Itron

Figure 1-23 Large meter, singlejet design

Compound Meters

The early history of meters included the development of various devices aimed at improving accuracy over a wide range of flows, including very low flows. This work resulted in the basic idea of a large turbine meter on the main line, a small meter on a bypass, and a valve to direct water to one meter or the other automatically. The registration was the total of the readings on the two meters on some designs and dual registers on other designs. The single-register design was covered in J.A. Tilden's initial Patent 742,136 of 1903.

In 1909, F.N. Connet's Patent 934,504 covered a single-register, compound meter with a pair of ratchet-wheel drives arranged such that the register was driven by whichever drive moved faster. This patent also showed the main-line meter mounted horizontally. It was the direct forerunner of the latest high-flow, single-register compound meters.

Much developmental effort has gone into the compounding valve to facilitate rapid opening and minimize loss of registration when changing from bypass to main-line registration. Modern swing-type and easy-lift valves require a pressure differential (developed by flow through the bypass meter) to start to open, but then move very easily to the full-open position. It is claimed that the single-register compounds suffer no changeover loss of accuracy as flow moves through the bypass and the mainline meters in series when the valve is open; therefore, whichever unit records the greater flow drives the register. Even though the single-register meter is easier to read, it must be inspected more frequently because trouble in one unit might not be readily apparent to the meter reader (Figures 1-24 and 1-25). The standard for compound meters is ANSI/AWWA C702, Cold-Water Meters—Compound Type.

Fire-Service Meters

Water utilities have found it necessary to meter lines that are typically used for everyday needs and are occasionally required to supply water for firefighting purposes. Insurance underwriters have demanded that such lines have no restriction that could interfere with full flow of water in the event of fire, even if the meter is jammed or damaged.

To meet this requirement and still provide metering, a meter was developed that is a combination of a proportional main-line meter and disc or compound bypass meter, as described in chapter 2. Several brands of meters have been approved for such use by Underwriters Laboratories (UL) and Factory Mutual Laboratories (FM). The first of these meters was approved in 1916.

The first known design was developed by J.A. Tilden, and the first meter was shipped by his company in 1908. His Patent 971,510 was issued in 1910 and is similar to the construction now used. Another idea, patented in 1913 by J.R. Freeman (Patent 1,057,721), used a Venturi-type, main-line meter. H. Chrisman's Patent 1,118,921 of 1914 covered a displacement meter for measuring small quantities. It was positioned in the main line but was swung out of the flow stream by a high flow rate so that the line was free of obstruction, but the meter was inoperative. In 1915, Patent 1,138,640 by H.I. Dilts was the basis of the other approved fire-service meter, which used a disc-type bypass meter and a disc-type proportional meter for high flows.

For installations where daily use is to be metered but not emergency main-line flow, the detector check has been developed. The detector check consists of (1) a weight-loaded valve in the main line that remains closed under normal usage, and (2) a bypass around this valve that contains a water meter to measure daily use. When full flow is required, the weight-loaded valve opens, as in a compound or fire-service

Figure 1-24 Compound meter, double-register type

Figure 1-25 Compound meter, single-register type

meter, and resistance in the main line is negligible. A very small quantity continues to flow through the metered bypass, on most models, when the detector check valve is open. In place of traditional check valves, bypass meters are also being used in conjunction with modern backflow devices.

ANSI/AWWA C703, Standard for Cold-Water Meters—Fire-Service Type, provides that fire-service meters shall consist of one of the following:

A. A combination of (1) a mainline meter of the proportional type, Underwriters Laboratories (UL) listed or Factory Mutual Research (FM) approved, having an unobstructed passageway of essentially the pipe size, for measuring high flow rates; (2) a bypass meter of the appropriate size for measuring low flow rates; and (3) an automatic valve for diverting flow rates other than fire demand through the bypass meter.

B. A combination of (1) a mainline meter of the turbine type (class II), UL listed or FM approved; (2) a UL-listed or FM-approved fire-service strainer; (3) a bypass meter of the appropriate size for measuring low flow rates; and (4) an automatic valve for diverting flow rates other than fire demand through the bypass meter.

C. A combination of (1) a mainline meter of the turbine type (class II), UL listed or FM approved; and (2) a UL-listed or FM-approved fire-service strainer.

Proportional Meters

The proportional meter measures a relatively constant but small percentage of the water flowing through the line. A multiplying factor is built into the meter register to record the total quantity that has passed through the main line. This task is accomplished by providing an expanded section of the line with a ring at the downstream end having an internal diameter equal to the nominal pipe diameter (see the fire-service meter shown in Figure 1-26). The restriction ring creates a drop in line pressure just below it, as compared with full line pressure upstream. This differential in pressure forces a proportion of the water through the small displacement-type bypass meter.

When correctly calibrated, a proportional meter is accurate within 3 percent over a 10-to-1 or 12-to-1 total flow range, depending on the size of the bypass meter relative to the main line. No AWWA standard covers only proportional meters because they are most commonly used as a fire-service meter.

Propeller Meters

The propeller meter was developed to (1) permit self-contained measurement of water velocity in large lines up to 72 in. (1,800 mm); (2) measure water containing impurities that might clog other types of meters; (3) provide a mechanical meter that would operate with an absolute minimum loss of pressure; and (4) permit saddle-mounting of the meter on a pipeline if required. These are technically classified as flowmeters, used for control/monitoring purposes, and are not normally used for billing purposes (Figure 1-27).

Accuracy provisions for propeller meters are contained in ANSI/AWWA C704, Standard for Propeller-Type Meters for Waterworks Applications.

Magnetic-Drive Meters

During the early use of water meters, there was a need to eliminate the accumulation of mud and fogging of the glass in register compartments of meters in pits or curb-box settings. The ventilation hole in the register compartment, by which the stuffing-box leakage could escape, also permitted moisture to condense beneath the glass and permitted mud to enter when meter pits were flooded by surface water. Reading of the meter was then impossible.

Three methods were tried to overcome this problem. During the 1930s and 1940s, some meters were built with the register glass capable of being lifted to read the dial beneath, but even more dirt could accumulate in the register compartment with this

Courtesy: Elster AMCO Water Inc.
Figure 1-26 Fire-service meter

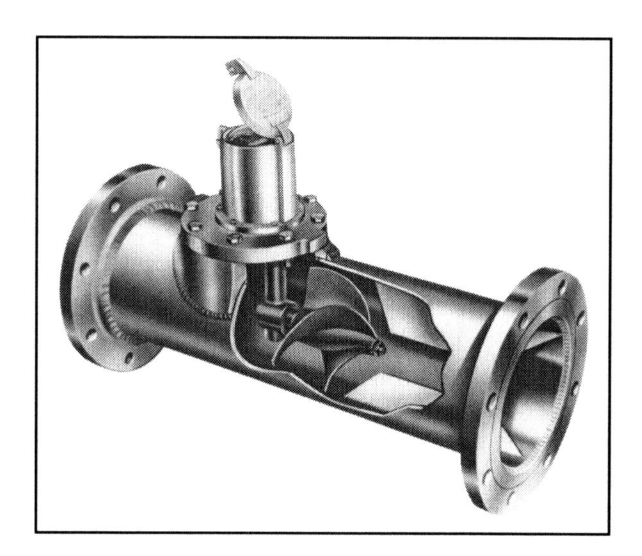

Figure 1-27 Propeller meter

design. In 1917 and again in the late 1940s, a design was developed that placed the register in a sealed compartment, with a small stuffing box on the register drive shaft. The register unit was then filled with oil. This device helped, but leakage of the oil was difficult to prevent.

In 1912 and again in 1934, two attempts were made to introduce meters with magnetically driven, sealed registers. Both meters were discontinued because of the undependable magnets available for the drives, which were not permanent. In 1956, the first of the modern magnetically driven meters was introduced. It was an oscillating-piston meter with a permanently sealed register unit containing both register and reducing gear train. The magnetic drive eliminated the stuffing box and shaft previously used to transmit motion from the measuring piston to the register and was made possible by the newly developed permanent magnets. A magnet mounted in the drive pin of the oscillating piston traced a circular path around a well extending downward from the register unit. A free follower, another permanent magnet, rolled around on the inside of the well, pushing a crank that drove the register unit.

During the following few years, practically all US meter manufacturers released magnetically driven, sealed register meter designs. In most cases, the reducing gear trains were removed from the inside of the main casing. In these meters, the pin in the center of the disc or piston engages a driver block centrally mounted on a shaft in the driver magnet unit. On the upper end of the shaft, a ceramic-face magnet is mounted. The rotative motion of the driver magnet is transmitted to a driven magnet of similar design through the bronze main casing, where it drives the gearing and register.

This design has two styles. In one style, the register assembly is factory permanently sealed, and no change gears are used (Figure 1-14). In the other, the register compartment can be opened in the meter shop for repair or for recalibration by the change gears (Figure 1-15). Both styles are considered sealed because, when assembled, the register is sealed against air and moisture, although change-gear-equipped registers are obsolete today due to high maintenance cost. In the latter style, a capsule containing a desiccant is placed in the register compartment to absorb any moisture in the air at the time the meter is assembled. Desiccants are also virtually obsolete today. In some designs, shields of soft magnetic metals protect the magnetic couple against external interference.

The result has been meters that are more sensitive to low flow and have a longer service life. Friction load on the measuring unit has been reduced by eliminating the heavy intermediate gear train and the packing gland or stuffing box and by the extensive use of low-friction, lightweight parts in the register. The sealed register, with its high-impact-resistant lens, has reduced both fogging and breakage of the lens and corrosion of the working parts and has allowed field replacement of the register without interruption of service.

ACCEPTANCE OF METERS BY WATER UTILITIES

The practice of charging for water by metering was questioned by water utilities for several years. One of the chief objections was that occupants of metered homes would attempt to keep water charges at a minimum by not using enough water for sanitary purposes. It was even reported that some users placed a tub under a faucet and allowed water to drip into the tub at a rate too slow for the meter to register. Water was dipped from the tub with a pail as needed.

This problem was solved by establishing a monthly minimum charge, for which enough water was furnished to provide for reasonable sanitary needs. No carryover of unused allowance to the next month was permitted. This method opened the way to universal metering, once improved meters were available, and it was determined that the total cost of operating a metered system was less than the cost without meters because water usage was reduced.

STANDARDIZATION

Standardization of meters in the United Stated began in 1913. Fortunately, standardization issues were considered at this time because otherwise a chaotic situation similar to one existing abroad might have resulted. The following paragraph from a paper delivered by R.P. Van Royen of Amsterdam, at a 1937 meeting of the Association of Water Supply Officials in Holland, illustrates this situation:

> The great diversity which prevails in water meters with respect to construction, to overall length, and to connections (both as to bore and as to screw thread) is well known. The responsibility for this state of affairs lies as much on the maker as on the user. The former (not only) followed his own constructive design, which was excusable, inasmuch as he intended thereby to supply the best that could be had, but also his own particular details, as, for example, the screw thread. Once he had secured for himself the acceptance of his thread in any district, he bettered his chance of excluding his competitors from that district. But, on the other hand, makers were prepared to meet their customers' wishes by supplying other

> details than their own regular ones. Feeble attempts at standardization—for example, of overall length and of connections—only led to an increased diversity. In the German literature on the subject, I noted a statement that one firm makes 65 types of 3-cu m meters (3 cu m/hr = 13 gpm), which is due, among other things, to fifteen different overall lengths, between 130 and 220 mm; eleven different threaded ends of diameters from 23 to 38 mm; besides flange joints of ten different patterns. The number of boxes for meters up to and including 40 mm was no less than 185.

An AWWA committee, appointed in 1913, proposed the adoption of standards on overall lengths and connections for disc meters in 1915 and 1916. In 1917, the New England Water Works Association (NEWWA) also proposed a set of standards. No official action was taken, however, on either proposal. In 1916, the meter manufacturers organized a meter standards committee, on which most manufacturers were represented.

On March 9–10, 1920, the AWWA and NEWWA committees met jointly to review drafts of a proposed standard developed by the manufacturers' committee. The final draft of the "Standard Specifications for Cold-Water Meters, Disc Type" was approved by AWWA and NEWWA in 1921. A revision was adopted by AWWA in 1946 and another in 1964. An important feature of the 1946 revision was the adoption of exact thread specifications for spuds on ⅝-in. (15-mm) to 1-in. (25-mm) meters and for coupling nuts. These specifications differ slightly from general thread specifications. They were selected to permit full interchangeability of new meters and/or couplings with old meters or couplings having various off-standard threads.

The title of the 1946 edition was broadened to "Displacement Meters" to include the oscillating-piston meter, and the 1964 edition is designated as a "standard" rather than a "specification." The revisions since 1971 include magnetic-drive meters and a ½-in. meter size. Standards for compound, fire-service, and current meters were first adopted in 1923; propeller meters were adopted in 1949; multijet meters were adopted in 1976; and plastic main-case meters were adopted in 1988. Standards for single-jet meters and fluidic-oscillator meters were adopted in 2002 and 2005, respectively. Standards are revised or reaffirmed at least every five years.

As this update to AWWA Manual M6 goes to press, electronic meters of the electromagnetic and ultrasonic types and/or electronically enhanced turbines are being introduced that offer potential alternatives to classic ANSI/AWWA C701-, C702-, and C704-type meters. See Figures 1-28, 1-29, and 1-30.

Courtesy: Master Meter Inc.

Figure 1-28 A 4-in. ultrasonic meter

Courtesy: Elster AMCO Water Inc.
Figure 1-29 A battery-powered electromagnetic meter

Courtesy: Sensus Metering Systems
Figure 1-30 A turbine meter with electronic enhancement

Capacity and Pressure-Loss Ratings

Early meters had high pressure loss for a given capacity. This loss was partly due to their complicated design and partly deliberate, to reduce the possibility of running the meter too fast, because damage to parts at excess speed was likely. The problem persisted even after the present simple disc or oscillating-piston designs were developed. Discs could break at excess speed, so some meters were fitted with different chamber settings to compensate for high line pressure.

The first AWWA "specifications," now known as "standards," were adopted in June 1921 and addressed disc meters. The manufacturers who aided the standards committee had to develop a workable, uniform standard for pressure-loss limits and capacity ratings. At the suggestion of R.S. Bassett, the ratio of the capacities of the various sizes was fixed by setting a constant peripheral speed of a point on the edge of the disc in its up-and-down motion as the basis of measure of relative capacity.

Because the ⅝-in. (15-mm) meter was already universally rated at 20 gpm (4.5 m^3/h), the rated capacities of the other sizes were set so that this speed was constant for all meter sizes.

The standards committee also agreed on a relatively uniform pressure loss for the different brands within the 20-psi (140-kPa) pressure-loss limit adopted at that time. Although this limit was too high for average use, meters seldom run at more than 50 percent of rated capacity. As the pressure loss increases with the square of the increase in rate of flow, a meter with a pressure loss of 20 psi (140 kPa) at safe rated capacity had a loss of only 5 psi (35 kPa) at 50 percent rating, which was permissible. Later water meter design improvements greatly reduced pressure loss. Average pressure loss in new ⅝-in. (15-mm) meters today is less than 15 psi (104 kPa) at 20 gpm (4.5 m^3/h).

Size Designations

The size of a water meter has always been described in terms of the size of pipe for which the meter was originally intended. When meters started to become popular in the United States, the standard pipe for residential services was lead pipe with an internal diameter of ⅝ in. (15 mm) and wiped solder joints. Consequently, meters were built with ⅝-in. (15-mm) inside diameter (ID) inlets and outlets. To permit a meter to be removed for servicing, its ends were threaded with ¾-in. (20-mm) straight external threads, and couplings of the same ⅝-in. (15-mm) ID were used. These couplings had a ¾-in. (20-mm) threaded nut on one end to fit the meter and a smooth tinned end on the tailpiece suitable for making the wiped joint to the pipe.

With the advent of galvanized-iron pipe services around the 1890s, the standard-size residential service had ½-in. (13-mm) ID pipe. The same meter couplings were used for this pipe, but ½-in. (13-mm) external-tapered iron-pipe threads were used on the tailpieces, retaining the ⅝-in. (15-mm) ID and the same connecting nuts to the meter body.

In 1896, one manufacturer, at a customer's request, built a ⅝-in. (15-mm) meter with connections for ¾-in. (20-mm) pipe. The sizes of the threads and couplings previously used on the full ¾-in. (20-mm) meter were used. The meter body then had 1-in. (25-mm) threads with ¾-in. (20-mm) couplings and was called the ⅝-in. (15-mm) by ¾-in. (20-mm) meter. This designation has become universal.

At present, threads on meter bodies having external-threaded ends are typically one nominal iron-pipe size (NPS) larger than the nominal size of the meter.

REMOTE-READING DEVICES

The first known remote-reading device, patented in 1890 by L. Ehrlich (Patent 428,900), was an electrically operated unit for gas meters. A water meter remote reader, also electric, was patented in 1917 by Edwin H. Ford and A. Neff (Patent 1,244,634). In 1957, the first of the modern remote readers was introduced for quantity sales. It consisted of an electric pulse generator driven by the meter with the pulses actuating a solenoid-operated counter at the remote location (Patent 3,118,075 issued to M.J. Dunn).

In 1959, a meter with a battery-powered readout was introduced. When it was inserted into a plug socket at the remote location, the wiring to the meter was energized. The position of the hands on the meter dial was transmitted electrically to dials on the readout instrument carried by the meter reader. Another type, a pneumatic pulse transmitter, appeared in 1967 and had a pulse-operated, remote counter.

Several sophisticated devices for digital encoding of readings are now offered that provide data entry to computers. The development of these devices has been recent and too complex for detailed description in this brief review. Further information on present types of remote-reading meters is given in chapter 9 and in ANSI/AWWA C706, Standard for Direct-Reading Remote-Registration Systems for Cold-Water Meters, and ANSI/AWWA C707, Standard for Encoder-Type Remote-Registration Systems for Cold-Water Meters.

PLASTIC PARTS AND COMPONENTS

Several of the major meter manufacturers started experimenting with the use of plastic materials in water meters around 1960. Engineered plastics were first used as a replacement for internal parts such as measuring chambers and then expanded to other parts such as the register. By 1970, most of the manufacturers had converted to plastics for certain parts in their water meters. By the mid-1970s, a number of utilities were using meters with plastic main cases.

Plastic main-case meters (Figure 1-31) require careful handling in the field during insertion into the meter setting to prevent cross threading or possible damage caused by misaligned meter settings. In the absence of a *metal* meter yoke, an electrical ground strap should be installed around either plastic or metal main-case meters in compliance with the National Electrical Code. Register lenses of plastic material are more easily scratched than glass and can obscure the register face if care is not exercised by meter readers when wiping the lens clean.

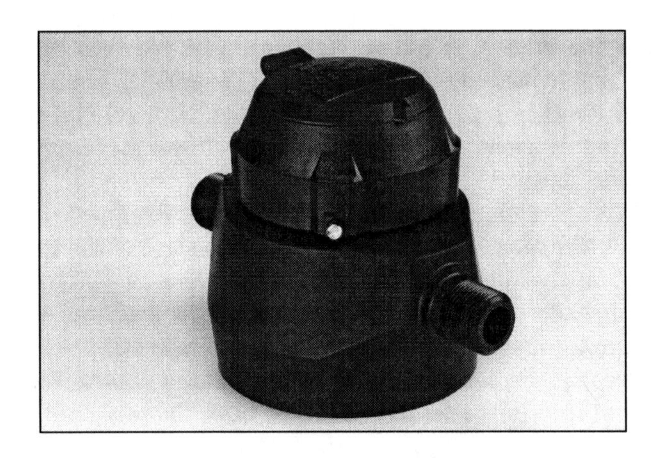

Courtesy: Badger Meter Inc.

Figure 1-31 Typical plastic-body small-disc meter

This page intentionally blank.

Chapter 2

Selecting Meter Types

INTRODUCTION

Selecting water meters for installations serving various types of customers usually presents a problem only when considering commercial or industrial accounts. However, apartment buildings, schools, other large establishments, and the combination of private fire service and general use through a single line (when permitted) also require consideration for satisfactory meter installation.

Selection involves both size and type of meter. Too often, size is chosen merely to match the pipe size; but oversized pipe is often installed to allow for possible future increases in water use or to reduce pressure loss in a long length of pipe. Chapter 3 discusses the method of calculating total friction loss, although the example covers only small services. Based on this principle, plus customer demand information, and pressure-loss data from meter manufacturers' catalogs, the meter size is selected. For example, if a 3-in. (80-mm) meter in a 4-in. (100-mm) line is appropriate, use of a 4-in. (100-mm) meter is inadvisable. It would be unnecessarily expensive, heavy to handle, and less accurate under overall usage conditions. However, it is advisable to provide a suitable transition and extra space in the pipeline and in the meter pit so that a larger meter can be installed later if usage increases.

Undoubtedly, the past tendency to install oversize meters resulted from the desire to use a meter large enough to meet the customer's maximum demands and not to incur additional expense, if a small meter became inadequate. However, with careful study of expected demand, the correct meter size can be determined in advance. A larger meter can be installed later, if necessary, if space is provided at the time of the original installation.

The type of meter to use is determined by the anticipated range of flow rates, plus allowable pressure loss and possible safety requirements (such as fire-service regulations). Several types are available, as shown in Table 2-1. This manual describes only the more common types; information on other meters can be obtained from the respective manufacturers. When calculating flow demand, it is important to consider meter type and suitability for use as a revenue-collecting metering device or a flow-monitoring device.

Table 2-1 Types of meters for water measurement

Type	Usual Range of Sizes	
	in.	*mm*
I. Displacement		
A. Nutating disc	½–2	13–50
B. Oscillating piston	½–2	13–50
II. Nondisplacement		
A. Velocity		
Multijet	⅝–2	15–50
Singlejet	⅝–6	15–150
Fluidic oscillator	½–2	13–50
Magnetic-pickup turbine	¼–12	6–300
Turbine	¾–20	20–500
Propeller	2–72	50–1,800
Proportional	3–12	80–300
B. Differential pressure		
Fixed opening, variable differential		
Orifice	2–24	50–600
Venturi, flow nozzle, flow tube	2–84	50–2,100
Pitot tube	Unlimited	
Variable opening, fixed differential rotameter	¼–4	6–100
C. Electronic velocity		
Electromagnetic	⅒–72	2–1,800
Ultrasonic	½–72	13–1,800
D. Level measurement		
Weir, Parshall flume, etc.	Unlimited	
III. Compound		
A. Standard compound	2–8	50–200
B. Fire service	3–12	80–300

SMALL FLOWS

In the United States and Canada, the standard meter in 2-in. (50-mm) and smaller sizes has been the displacement meter, of which there are two variations, the nutating piston (disc) and the oscillating piston. Essentially equal in performance, these meters have proven by experience to be unrivaled for their combination of accuracy, long life, simple design, moderate cost, and easy maintenance. Tens of millions of these meters are in use. Since the 1960s, multijet meters have been successfully used in the same applications. Multijet meters are covered in ANSI/AWWA C708, Standard for Cold-Water Meters—Multijet Type.

In the 1990s, singlejet technology was introduced from Europe. Singlejet meters have since been in use for small-meter applications. These meters are covered in ANSI/AWWA C712, Standard for Cold-Water Meters—Singlejet Type, the first edition of which was approved in 2002.

In addition, major advancements have been made in the area of small electronic meters designed primarily for residential service. These include the fluidic-oscillator, ultrasonic, and electromagnetic meters.

The standard for fluidic-oscillator meters is ANSI/AWWA C713, Standard for Cold-Water Meters—Fluidic-Oscillator Type. ANSI/AWWA C750, Standard for Transit-Time Flowmeters in Full Closed Conduits, addresses transit-time ultrasonic flowmeters used in a variety of applications as flow-monitoring devices (rate measurement); it does not apply to revenue-collecting metering devices specifically. As of 2012, AWWA does not have a standard for electromagnetic meters.

Most residential services are metered with the ⅝-in. (15-mm) size having ¾-in. (20-mm) connections. For information on capacity in relation to pressure loss, see chapter 3. Note that normal flows should not be more than approximately one-half of the maximum capacity if long life is the objective.

Today, small magnetic-drive meters have very low pressure loss and a much longer life than older models.

MEDIUM FLOWS

For services that can be metered with 1½-in. (40-mm) meters, the displacement, multijet, or singlejet meter can be used. The low-flow accuracy of modern 1½-in. (40-mm) meters is excellent, and compound meters are not usually manufactured in sizes less than 2 in. (50 mm). Where low-flow accuracy is not important, as in services used only for filling tanks at rapid flow, the 1½-in. (40-mm) turbine meter may be operated safely at a higher average rate than the displacement meter.

The 2-in. (50-mm) displacement, multijet, turbine, singlejet, and compound meters have their places and their advocates. Those who prefer the displacement meter have indicated that it is simpler to use, is lower in cost, and records consumption remarkably well at low flow rates. Proponents of the compound meter emphasize that it is more accurate on very low flows or leaks and has lower pressure loss at high flow rates. Proponents of the multijet and singlejet meters emphasize their quiet operation and their ability to pass dirt particles and other entrained flow debris. The life expectancy of any meter will be greatly limited if exposed to excessive debris.

The choice between compound and turbine meters in 3-in. (80-mm) to 4-in. (100-mm) sizes appears to be determined by the average flow rates to be measured. If close accuracy at very low flows is important, but large capacity is also needed, the compound meter should be used. If large capacity is of primary importance, flows are usually above 10 percent of maximum rating, and low-flow accuracy is secondary, the turbine meter should be used, especially one of the newer models with very low pressure loss.

LARGE FLOWS

For lines 3 in. and larger, the traditional choice of meters is the compound, turbine, singlejet, propeller, or fire-service meter. Ultrasonic and electromagnetic meters are now an option for this type of application, though currently AWWA does not publish a standard on these meter types for revenue-collecting purposes.

For some light commercial or larger living complexes (condos, apartments, and motels), the compound meter is frequently purchased. This type of meter registers well over the widest flow range and has relatively low pressure loss at high flow rates. There are two variations of compound meter design.

In the first, or parallel meter, the main-line meter does not operate until the compounding valve opens. The bypass meter may or may not continue operating when the main-line meter starts. If this meter has two registers, and if either unit fails, the trouble can be detected by the stoppage of its register.

In the second, or series meter, when the compounding valve is closed, water flows through the main-line meter and then through the bypass meter. When the pressure differential in the bypass meter is great enough to cause the compounding valve to open, the main-line meter is already running. The register is driven by a pair of ratchet drives, allowing the unit that is producing more registration to drive the register. The main-line unit is not required to start from rest at the changeover point.

All compound meters lose a certain degree of accuracy operating within the changeover flow range by varying amounts. It is important to size any compound meter installation to minimize the total flow each installation experiences in the changeover flow range.

Turbine and current meters, including electronic flowmeters, are used when flows are large, minimum flows are usually above 10 or 12 percent of maximum rating, and the low-pressure loss at high flows is valuable. These meters have a separate inner measuring chamber or cage, which may be removed with the rotor for servicing. ANSI/ AWWA C701, Standard for Cold-Water Meters—Turbine Type, for Customer Service, divides turbine meters into class I and class II meters. Both classes of meters register by recording the revolutions of a turbine set in motion by the force of flowing water striking the blades. Class I turbine meters are the vertical-shaft and low-velocity, horizontal-shaft models. Class II turbine meters are in-line, horizontal-axis, high-velocity turbines characterized by lower head loss and wider normal test-flow limits. Magnetic flowmeters are covered in AWWA Manual M33, *Flowmeters in Water Supply.*

Propeller meters are intended for main-line or pump station discharge measurements. They operate with the minimum of pressure loss for a mechanical meter. In small propeller meters, the propeller is built into a section of pipe of precise diameter and forms part of the meter; in large sizes, saddlemounting of the propeller is customary, with the interior of the pipe serving as the measuring tube. At the point of measurement, the velocity profile should be uniform. This requires that there are no elbows, valves, constrictions, or enlargements in the pipe for several pipe diameters of distance upstream and for a lesser distance downstream. For detailed instructions, users should consult the manufacturer of the proposed meter.

Where fire hydrants or large sprinkler systems are served by the metered line, the insurance underwriters usually insist on using a fire-service meter. Where these service conditions are encountered, the applicable insurance requirements should be ascertained before the meter is selected. Fire-service meters permit day-to-day usage to be drawn from a line serving hydrants or sprinklers, with the entire flow metered. For detecting the unauthorized use of water in lines for unmetered fire-service applications, a unit called a detector check, double check detector assembly, or reduced pressure principle detector assembly is installed. This same construction permits authorized metered use of small quantities of water from a fire-service line.

The detector check meter, a UL-listed, FM-approved device, is designed for dedicated fire-service applications. These devices are not intended to meter consumption; rather, utilities use these devices to detect leaks and unauthorized water usage. A second, normally smaller, service line is installed with an appropriately sized water meter for measurement of normal domestic water consumption.

Consider, for example, a warehouse that requires a high volume of water flow for fire protection but may also have a small bathroom and maybe a coffee maker. By utilizing a detector check meter for the fire-service and a second domestic-service line, the utility can save on initial cost and ongoing maintenance compared to the cost of a fire-service meter.

Detector check meters consist of an automatic-weight or spring-loaded main check valve with an elastomer seal, a bypass piping system that incorporates a ⅝ × ¾ in. meter, ¾ in. check valve, ¾ in. ball valves, and a meter test valve. In operation, the main-line valve is held closed by the weight or spring with any low flow being directed through and measured by the bypass meter. When the pressure loss through the bypass reaches the engineered main valve opening point (normally a pressure loss of 1 to 2 psi or approximately 5 to 10 gpm), the main valve opens automatically, allowing full flow for emergencies. Water continues to be measured through the bypass meter, but flow though the main check valve is unmetered.

The detector check meter is the appropriate device for most commercial and industrial fire systems. If, however, the water is from an outside source or additives are present for antifreeze, regulatory agencies for fire-protection systems require a testable backflow preventer. These double check or reduced pressure devices are also available with metered bypasses. AWWA Manual M14, *Recommended Practice for Backflow Prevention and Cross-Connection Control,* contains more information.

Like all measurement devices, detector check meters require some maintenance to ensure proper operation. While the main valve assembly can be virtually maintenance-free, the bypass meter requires examination to ensure continued operation. By opening the meter test valve located downstream of the meter, a small amount of water is vented to the atmosphere, and the dial should be checked to ensure proper meter operation. Because the meter is being used as a tattletale and not as an accurate consumption-measuring device, volumetric accuracy is of less importance. It is very important that the meter register a small flow to detect leaks and unauthorized use. The main check valve elastomer sealing can be tested by setting up a differential pressure (DP) gauge to ensure that a differential pressure of 1 to 2 psi is maintained. This test is done by simply removing the meter and installing the appropriate DP gauge fittings.

Detector check meters can be installed inside a building or outside in a vault. Weight-loaded check valves require horizontal installation for proper operation, whereas spring-loaded valves can be installed horizontally or vertically on the fire-system standpipe.

It is common for utilities to ask building owners to remove a detector check and install a fire-service meter if consumption is registered more than once annually. Normal consumption should occur during the annual fire system test. The selection of the proper device for each application and an understanding of the limitations of a metering device will ensure that the highest value is obtained.

Other types of meters for large lines include the Venturi or its modifications, the flow tube, or the flow nozzle. These meters differ from the other meters because they measure by differential pressure instead of by velocity or quantity. Flow ranges for accuracy vary with size and with details of design, so information should be obtained from the manufacturer of the meter. Although built in smaller sizes, these meters usually are used in 6-in. (150-mm) or larger lines.

Improvements in the microprocessor readouts for both electromagnetic and ultrasonic large electronic velocity meters have enabled these devices to have not only raw and wastewater applications, but also to apply to nonrevenue measurement of finished water and water treatment chemicals. Both meters offer the advantage of an unobstructed flow tube with no moving parts and high accuracy; both, however, require electronic power.

For temporary measurements, the Pitot tube may be used in main lines. In the hands of skilled operators, the meter is valuable in making surveys to ascertain rates of flow in large lines, to locate leaks, and to measure the flow from fire hydrants.

Manifolding of Meters

For 3-in. (80-mm) or larger lines, instead of using one meter to measure the entire flow, multiple smaller-sized meters are installed in a manifold (also called a battery). Typically, a manifold should consist of two meters or more, with each meter one pipe size or more smaller than the main line (e.g., two 2-in. [50-mm] meters in a 3-in. [80-mm] manifold). For example, on a 3-in. (80-mm) line, the manifold may consist of two displacement meters. On a 6-in. (150-mm) or 10-in. (250-mm) line, the manifold may consist of two or three compound or turbine meters. All meters in a manifold should be of the same brand, model (type), and size.

Branch manifolds are only recommended if there is close coordination of the technical details with the meter manufacturer or other experts in flow hydraulics. It is imperative that the flow through the multiple branches be balanced for proper meter registration and performance. Figure 4-5 illustrates a typical 3-meter and 2-meter hydraulically balanced manifold of large meters.

Manifolding of meters has the following advantages:

1. One meter can be serviced by closing its shutoff valves while the water supply is still available to the customer through the other meter.
2. Since the meters within the manifold are smaller than a single meter for the same service, fewer personnel are required for meter servicing or removal.
3. Inventory of repair parts can be minimized, and the knowledge of repair and testing techniques can be less involved when the variety of size and type of meters in the system is controlled.
4. The manifold can be side-wall mounted to conserve floor space.

Chapter 3

Effects of Water-Flow Friction, Increased Usage, and Pressure Losses on Service Adequacy

INTRODUCTION

Careful consideration should be given to a service-line installation to ensure that it will provide an adequate supply of water to a customer. Frequently, new water services are sized and installations made based on experience. However, although experience does contribute considerably to a satisfactory and adequate supply, other important factors must be evaluated. It is possible to have adjacent installations that vary by peak demand to such an extent that they are not identical. Each installation should be considered individually, and the proper size installation made initially. After startup, changes are expensive and often impossible to make.

FACTORS TO CONSIDER IN SIZING MAINS

The following are important factors to consider in sizing mains:

- Water demand and expected usage.
- Pressure and volume of water presently available and in the future at the point-of-service connection in the main. Projected future installations should also be considered.
- Pressure loss, due to differences in elevation between the main and building, known as elevation head.

- Water-flow friction in the service line from the main in the street to the curb or property line.
- Water-flow friction in the service line from the curb or property line to the building.
- Pressure loss through the meter and valves.
- Pressure loss and water-flow friction in the building.

The utility is responsible for providing an adequate supply of water at sufficient pressure to its customers. In addition to meeting present or initial demands, anticipated usage should be considered as well. Mains are often extended to accommodate new housing developments. This increased water usage could cause less water to be available and at lower pressure. Therefore, the service installation to a building should be slightly larger under these circumstances to compensate for the expected supply variance.

Sufficient pressure must exist in the main to elevate the water to the building. It is obvious that if the installation is high above the main, for example on a hill, more pressure is required to deliver the water than if it were in a valley below. One psi of pressure will raise water 27.7 in. or 2.31 ft (0.704 m) in a vertical pipe. This is called elevation head, and the total difference in elevation head of an installation must be subtracted from the available main pressure when considering available operating pressure. When the dwelling is below the main (Table 3-1), the available operating pressure increases, and the elevation head may be added to main pressure (at the rate of 1 psi [6.9 kPa] for every 2.31 ft [0.704 m] in height). The distance from the main to the property line may vary in each installation, especially when the main is placed along one side of the street and service must be made to both.

Friction loss, due to water flow through the service line from the property line to the building, must also be considered. The differences not only between tubing of various sizes, but between copper and plastic tubing, are illustrated in Table 3-2. Both disc and oscillating-piston meters, if they are to meet AWWA standards, must be manufactured to the stated material and performance requirements. Consequently, both have comparable pressure-loss features. The pressure losses shown in Table 3-3 are averages and were computed using a 10-psi (69-kPa) pressure loss at maximum flow for all-size meters. This is an ample figure for estimating flow and is applicable to both meters. Actual figures can be obtained from the manufacturer of the meter and used in the calculations. It is difficult, and of little importance, to show in detail the differences between all meters manufactured, because the difference is slight when the meters are of similar size.

As a general rule, the water utility does not have the responsibility for or control over the pipe size and fittings within a customer's building, so allowance must be made for reasonable customer pressure losses and adequate flow provided. Automatic washing machines, dishwashers, garbage disposals, and multiple bathrooms have created the need for more flow-rate capacity; consequently, service requirements have increased considerably. In order to provide an adequate water-supply pressure, losses must be minimized in the service installation.

FRICTION-LOSS DATA

Table 3-2 has been compiled from computed data to illustrate the relationship and comparative pressure loss between copper tubing, plastic tubing made to iron-pipe ID dimensions, and plastic tubing made to copper-tube OD dimensions. It should be noted that no reference has been made to, nor has the table included, data for ½-in. (13-mm) service tubing, either copper or plastic. This omission was deliberate to discourage

Table 3-1 Elevation above supply main—elevation head

Elevation to Building, *ft*	Head, *psi*	Elevation to Building, *ft*	Head, *psi*
1	0.433	14	6.062
2	0.866	15	6.495
3	1.299	16	6.928
4	1.732	17	7.361
5	2.165	18	7.794
6	2.598	19	8.227
7	3.031	20	8.660
8	3.464	21	9.093
9	3.897	22	9.526
10	4.330	23	9.959
11	4.763	24	10.392
12	5.196	25	10.825
13	5.629		

Note: Other values of elevation head can be calculated by multiplying actual elevation, in feet, by 0.433 (head at 1 ft).

Metric Conversions: ft × 0.3048 = m, psi × 6.89476 = kPa.

Table 3-2 Comparison of computed water flow friction losses for service line, *psi/ft*

	¾ in.			1 in.			1¼ in.	
Flow Rate *gpm*	Copper Tube	Plastic* Iron Pipe ID	Plastic Copper Tube OD	Copper Tube	Plastic* Iron Pipe ID	Plastic Copper Tube OD	Copper Tube	Plastic* Iron Pipe ID
1	0.003	0.002	0.005					
2	0.008	0.005	0.013					
3	0.016	0.010	0.026					
4	0.025	0.015	0.041					
5	0.037	0.024	0.065	0.009	0.007	0.022		
6	0.048	0.031	0.081	0.011	0.008	0.029		
7	0.063	0.041	0.108	0.018	0.011	0.038		
8	0.075	0.049	0.128	0.021	0.013	0.045		
9	0.095	0.062	0.160	0.026	0.017	0.057		
10	0.121	0.078	0.203	0.035	0.021	0.072		
11	0.166	0.108	0.274	0.057	0.040	0.104		
12	0.192	0.128	0.317	0.069	0.048	0.126		
13	0.206	0.134	0.338	0.071	0.050	0.130		
14	0.228	0.149	0.377	0.086	0.059	0.156		
15	0.263	0.169	0.428	0.107	0.076	0.200		
20	0.433	0.286	0.734	0.120	0.085	0.225	0.042	0.030
25	0.656	0.429	1.118	0.226	0.136	0.343	0.059	0.046
30	0.920	0.599		0.242	0.188	0.450	0.083	0.060
35		0.809		0.370	0.254	0.611	0.108	0.076
40				0.411	0.317	0.763	0.135	0.091
45				0.517	0.397	0.924	0.156	0.109
50				0.623	0.482	1.100	0.200	0.131
55				0.749	0.583		0.234	0.161
60				0.892	0.685		0.278	0.185

* Plastic per AWWA C901, Tables 2 and 3.

Metric Conversions: gpm × 0.2268 = m^3/h, in. × 25.4 = mm, psi/ft × 22.62 = kPa/m.

Table 3-3 Computed pressure losses for service components, *psi*

Flow Rate	Corporation Stop		Curb Stop		Globe Valve		Gate or Ball Valve		Meter		
	¾[*]	1[†]	¾[‡]	1[§]	¾[**]	1[††]	¾[‡‡]	1[§§]	⅝	¾	1
gpm	*in.*		*in.*		*in.*		*in.*		*in.*		
1	0.015	0.004	0.011	0.003	0.060	0.017					
2	0.050	0.014	0.034	0.008	0.195	0.058	0.001				
3	0.103	0.029	0.071	0.017	0.301	0.09	0.002				
4	0.170	0.03	0.117	0.028	0.664	0.20	0.003		0.39		
5	0.246	0.07	0.170	0.04	0.962	0.29	0.005	0.002	0.62		
6	0.340	0.11	0.234	0.05	1.33	0.43	0.007	0.002	0.89	0.39	
7	0.457	0.14	0.315	0.07	1.79	0.57	0.009	0.004	1.22	0.53	
8	0.557	0.17	0.384	0.08	2.18	0.71	0.011	0.004	1.60	0.71	0.25
9	0.703	0.22	0.485	0.10	2.75	0.85	0.013	0.005	2.02	0.89	0.32
10	0.879	0.23	0.606	0.13	3.44	1.0	0.016	0.007	2.50	1.10	0.39
11	1.20	0.28	0.72	0.15	4.08	1.2	0.020	0.009	3.00	1.35	0.48
12	1.31	0.32	0.83	0.18	4.72	1.4	0.024	0.011	3.60	1.60	0.57
13	1.40	0.37	0.94	0.21	5.36	1.6	0.028	0.013	4.20	1.88	0.67
14	1.54	0.42	1.05	0.24	6.00	1.8	0.032	0.015	4.90	2.18	0.77
15	1.70	0.47	1.17	0.27	6.64	2.0	0.036	0.017	5.60	2.50	0.89
16	2.11	0.53	1.31	0.30	7.46	2.3	0.040	0.019	6.40	2.85	1.02
17	2.25	0.59	1.45	0.34	8.28	2.6	0.044	0.021	7.20	3.22	1.16
18	2.36	0.65	1.60	0.38	9.10	2.9	0.049	0.023	8.10	3.60	1.30
19	2.54	0.72	1.75	0.42	9.93	3.2	0.054	0.025	9.00	4.00	1.45
20	2.75	0.80	1.90	0.46	10.76	3.5	0.059	0.028	10.00	4.45	1.60
25		1.2		0.67		5.1		0.047		7.10	2.50
30		1.6		0.92		7.0		0.062		10.00	3.60
35		2.1		1.2		9.0		0.077			4.80
40		2.7		1.5		11.6		0.086			6.40
45		3.3		1.9		14.6		0.093			8.10
50		4.0		2.3		17.6		0.130			10.00

[*] Based on equivalent loss of 5.86 ft of ¾-in. copper tubing.
[†] Based on equivalent loss of 6.67 ft of 1-in. copper tubing.
[‡] Based on equivalent loss of 4.04 ft of ¾-in. copper tubing.
[§] Based on equivalent loss of 3.85 ft of 1-in. copper tubing.
[**] Based on equivalent loss of 22.90 ft of ¾-in. copper tubing.
[††] Based on equivalent loss of 29.1 ft of 1-in. copper tubing.
[‡‡] Based on equivalent loss of 0.14 ft of ¾-in. copper tubing.
[§§] Based on equivalent loss of 0.21 ft of 1-in. copper tubing.

Metric Conversions: gpm × 0.2268 = m^3/h, in. × 25.4 = mm, psi × 6.89476 = kPa.

the use of this size. Pressure loss is considerably higher (approximately five times at 10 gpm [2.3 m^3/h]) through ½-in. (13-mm) copper tubing when compared with the ¾-in. (20-mm) size. Since the difference in initial material cost is negligible with identical installation, ½-in. (13-mm) service lines are not recommended.

Careful review of Table 3-2 will disclose that data are shown in pounds per square inch per linear foot. This enables the user to multiply the length of service line by the factor shown for the required flow rate. As an illustration, the water-friction loss through 88 ft (26.8 m) of ¾-in. (20-mm) copper tubing at 15 gpm (3.4 m^3/h) is 0.263 × 88 = 23.14 psi (159.5 kPa), whereas the loss through ¾-in. (20-mm) plastic tubing, iron-pipe ID size, is 0.169 × 88 = 14.87 psi (102.5 kPa).

SAMPLE SERVICE INSTALLATION CALCULATION

When an actual installation is calculated, all necessary facts should be available. For the purpose of illustration, a hypothetical service will be considered. The water-supply main is 5 ft (1.5 m) below the pavement. The length of the service line from the water main to the property line is 43 ft (13.1 m) and 88 ft (26.8 m) from the property line to the meter. The meter is to be installed in the basement of a two-story dwelling, 21 ft (6.4 m) above the pavement. The main water pressure available at the corporation connection is 63 psi (435 kPa). Assume a household flow-rate requirement of 15 gpm (3.4 m^3/h) and 30-psi (210-kPa) pressure. This rate will vary depending on the number of residents and the household water-using equipment. (See Table 3-4 for theoretical discharge from various fixtures.) Actual discharge is usually less, due to rough, casting surface, etc. If pressure at the fixtures is above approximately 80 psi (550 kPa), a pressure-reducing valve should be installed in the system to avoid excessive force of water flowing from the fixtures.

Because the water-supply main is 5 ft (1.5 m) below the pavement, and the meter is 21 ft (6.4 m) higher than the pavement, the total elevation head to the meter is 26 ft (7.9 m). Table 3-1 is shown only to 25 ft (7.6 m), but the total elevation head can be calculated by multiplying 26 × 0.433, which equals 11.26 psi (77.6 kPa) (see table footnote). This figure must be added to the 30-psi (210-kPa) operating pressure required to service the fixtures and faucets in the building in order to obtain the operating pressure required at the main. A ¾-in. (20-mm) service will be considered and calculated. If a ¾-in. (20-mm) corporation stop is installed (Table 3-3), the pressure loss will be 1.70 psi (11.7 kPa). The total water-flow friction must now be calculated by adding the length of tubing from main to property line, 43 ft (13.1 m), and the distance the meter is to the property line, 88 ft (26.8 m), for a total of 131 ft (39.9 m). Table 3-2 shows that, for each foot of ¾-in. (20-mm) copper tubing, the friction loss at 15 gpm (3.4 m^3/h) is 0.263 psi (1.81 kPa). Consequently, when this figure is multiplied by the total of 131 ft (39.9 m), the total friction loss in the tubing is 34.45 psi (237.5 kPa). The total pressure required at the main is 77.41 psi (533.7 kPa). Based on this data, the system must be redesigned, because only 63 psi (434.4 kPa) is available at the main, and the meter and valve losses have not been considered.

In recalculation, the elevation head will not change, even though the supply lines are increased in size (elevation head is constant and irrespective of diameter). Consequently, it remains 11.26 psi (77.6 kPa). The water-flow friction through 131 ft (39.9 m) of 1-in. (25-mm) copper tubing is 14.01 psi (96.6 kPa); through a corporation stop 1 in. (25 mm) in size the friction is 0.47 psi (3.24 kPa); and building loss is 30 psi (210 kPa); for a total of 55.74 psi (384.3 kPa). Available distribution system pressure is 63 psi (434.4 kPa). Consequently, 7.26 psi (50.0 kPa) remains for the meter shutoff valve and the meter. Table 3-3 shows that pressure loss through a ⅝-in. (15-mm) meter at 15 gpm (3.4 m^3/h) is 5.60 psi (38.6 kPa), and the 1-in. (25-mm) ball valve (or gate valve) is less than the remaining available 1.66 psi (11.4 kPa). This new system will provide sufficient water at the dwelling.

The minimum available water pressure may be used in the calculation for pressure loss. It is not necessary to have extra or reserved pressure, but it is necessary to calculate the friction and pressure properly and consider all variables. Increasing the pressure loss or flow friction by miscalculation will decrease the available flow rate, but it will not stop the flow. Flow can be stopped only by an obstruction, such as a closed valve.

Table 3-4 Discharge from fixtures and faucets at various operating pressures

Type of Fixture or Faucet	Operating Pressure 5 *psi*	30 *psi*	90 *psi*
	Discharge *gpm*		
¾-in. compression sink faucet:			
Wide open	8.1	20.0	33.4
Half open	7.6	19.0	32.9
One-fourth open	7.0	17.4	29.9
½-in. compression sink faucet, wide open	6.0	14.8	24.5
½-in. ground key sink faucet, wide open	9.5	23.4	36.4
¾-in. ground key sink faucet, wide open	13.8	31.7	51.0
¾-in. compression sink faucet, wide open	9.0	22.1	36.0
½-in. self-closing compression faucet, wide open	2.6	6.8	11.7
⅜-in. ground key sink faucet, wide open	6.8	16.7	27.7
⅜-in. compression sink faucet, wide open	3.2	8.2	14.1
½-in. compression sink faucet, wide open	4.8	12.3	21.3
½-in. compression laundry tray faucet, open	6.3	17.3	25.3
Compression wash basin, wide open	5.0	11.9	21.3
1-in. ground key sink faucet, wide open	30.7	78.9	118.8
1-in. compression sink faucet, wide open	12.7	39.9	64.8
Combination compression laundry faucet:			
Both outlets open	9.6	22.4	38.6
Either hot or cold, wide open	6.1	14.4	24.8
Combination compression bath tub:			
Both hot and cold open, no nozzle	8.0	20.4	34.4
Both hot and cold open, with nozzle	5.9	14.3	24.8
Either hot or cold only, open, no nozzle	4.3	11.1	19.9
Either hot or cold only, open, with nozzle	3.8	9.2	16.1
Combination compression sink faucet with swinging nozzle:			
Hot and cold open	4.6	12.2	21.4
Either hot or cold open	3.2	8.4	14.8
Water closets:			
Tank type	2.9	8.0	14.6
Flush valves	9.7	30.0	45.7

Metric Conversions: psi × 6.89476 = kPa, gpm × 0.2268 = m^3/h, in. × 25.4 = mm.

When systems are designed for large meters, the same technique is used for calculating the pressure loss and flow friction. The size of the pipe, of course, will be different from that shown in the tables, and new values will be required for the flow rates. The elevation head remains constant, and only the flow friction changes, according to the flow rate and pipe size. Turbine, compound, and propeller meters have different flow characteristics, and the flow rate could vary considerably. When these meters are designed into a system, the manufacturer should be consulted for pressure loss information.

Frequently, after a service is in operation, the demand for water will increase. It is possible to increase the supply by replacing inadequate pipe or valves with material that has less pressure loss. However, it is desirable to have the correct-sized meter (as determined by the utility) installed, so that maximum accuracy at minimum flow can be realized. Information discussed in this chapter is covered more extensively in AWWA Manual M22, *Sizing Water Service Lines and Meters.*

Chapter 4

Meter Installation

INTRODUCTION

Water meters for customer service are installed, or set, in two ways: indoor and outdoor settings. In an indoor setting, the meter is installed inside the customer's premises, usually in the basement. In an outdoor setting, the meter is installed underground in a pit or meter box, which is usually located at the curb end of the service line. Historically, indoor settings have been used primarily in northern states where severe winter weather may cause frost damage, and outdoor settings have been used in warm, temperate climates.

INDOOR VERSUS OUTDOOR SETTINGS

The advantages of outdoor settings include meter location at point of delivery to customer; elimination of a separate curb box; reduction in meter damage from water heater failure; and no need to enter the customer's home for reading, inspection, and replacement. Disadvantages of outdoor settings include high costs when frost protection is required; reading difficulty; high maintenance due to flooding or snow; damage due to vandalism; liability exposure from the public for tripping accidents; and possible pit modifications due to grade changes.

The advantages of indoor settings include potentially lower installation costs; reduced damage and maintenance through elimination of exposure to outdoor conditions; for some utilities, the opportunity for customer contact via the meter reader; and the extended life of components such as AMR systems. Disadvantages of indoor settings include missed readings because of entry problems; hot-water damage; basement flooding due to frost-protective-bottom fracture or miscellaneous leaks; and consumer complaints about meter readers.

Remote Registers

The advent of inexpensive and reliable remote-meter-reading devices, which can be read manually or automatically, has added installation capabilities that modify and, in some cases, eliminate the previously accepted advantages and disadvantages of indoor versus outdoor settings. For example, it is now possible to read meters set indoors from outside the house and eliminate entry or call-back problems. It is also possible to read outside meters installed in pits without removing meter pit lids by using aboveground, mounted remote or automatic reading devices mounted in pit lids.

With the flexibility of remote registers, the utility manager can set meters to achieve minimum installation costs as well as minimum meter-reading costs. Because of the economic advantages of bringing indoor meter readings to the outside of the house, most remote-reading devices have initially been installed in northern areas. Remote-reading devices are now offered by all domestic meter manufacturers and are described in chapter 9. These devices offer an alternative in areas where outdoor pit settings have traditionally been used. The decision can now be made on the basis of overall economics, considering initial investment, installation cost, reading cost, and maintenance expense. Elimination of pit hazards, public injury liability, and pit maintenance should also be considered.

METER INSTALLATION

In addition to special considerations for indoor and outdoor meter settings, large meter settings and turbine meter installations also have special requirements. This section includes general considerations applicable to all meter installations and their related special needs.

General Considerations

Although standard specifications exist for meters, valves, pipe, and tubing, there are no standards for meter settings; however, certain principles should be observed. Specific problems and questions related to installation can best be addressed by consulting manufacturers of meters or setting and testing equipment. Over the years, a wealth of experience has been accumulated to provide meter settings that ensure optimum meter performance and service accessibility, along with ease of installation and low cost. Installation hardware is available in a wide variety of sizes, types, and materials to meet virtually any installation preferences or requirements. Many cities, counties, and states have adopted standards and ordinances under building plumbing codes to cover water meter installations.

Basic requirements of an acceptable meter installation are as follows:

1. Position meter in horizontal plane for optimum meter performance.
2. Locate meter so that it is readily accessible for reading, servicing, and/or testing.
3. Provide leak-tight, permanent setting to ensure that the meter can be removed from service without negatively affecting customer's plumbing.
4. Provide for permanent electrical grounding that does not use the meter to prevent accidental shock to meter service personnel.
5. Protect meter from freezing and other conditions that could damage the installation.
6. Provide high-quality inlet shutoff valve to allow meter maintenance. Location of meter may also dictate a meter valve on outlet side to prevent water draining back when meter is removed.
7. Provide a minimum loss of pressure.
8. Consider public safety and design installation to prevent accidents.

To avoid future operating problems, all open connections should be capped whenever a meter is removed from its setting for any length of time. A meter idler can be used in place of caps to provide the same protection. Also, meters should be protected from heat and direct sunlight during storage and transit prior to installation or after removal.

On all indoor settings, it is highly important that electrical continuity be maintained through the water line. Most utilities require electrical bonding around meters to prevent accidental electrocution of service personnel changing meters. If the meter setting itself does not provide a continuous electrical circuit when the meter is removed, a permanently bonded electrical grounding strap should be provided. Electrical grounding is a requirement specified by the National Electrical Code, and all service and installation personnel should be advised of this safety requirement. Most commercially available, prepared meter settings provide a continuous metallic circuit, even when the meter is removed from the line. AWWA opposes the grounding of electrical systems to pipe systems conveying drinking water to a customer's premises. Two types of commercially available meter settings are shown in Figure 4-1.

In the United States and several European countries, ample protection from backflow and backsiphonage is required in single family dwellings, as well as at commercial and industrial sites. The water supplier should be familiar with ANSI/AWWA C510, Standard for Double Check Valve Backflow Prevention Assembly, and ANSI/AWWA C511, Standard for Reduced-Pressure Principle Backflow Prevention Assembly, and the requirements of local, state, and federal authorities, whichever take precedence. This ensures that proper consideration will be given to the meter installation design, thereby providing for the required backflow preventers.

The selection of a fire-service meter type should follow the general guidelines for type selection for non-fire-line meters. Most commercial/industrial fire-line meter applications require a multi-register meter, but a separate fire line makes it possible to get by with a single fire-type turbine meter on the fire line. Figures 4-2 and 4-3 illustrate some issues regarding arrangements for residential fire service.

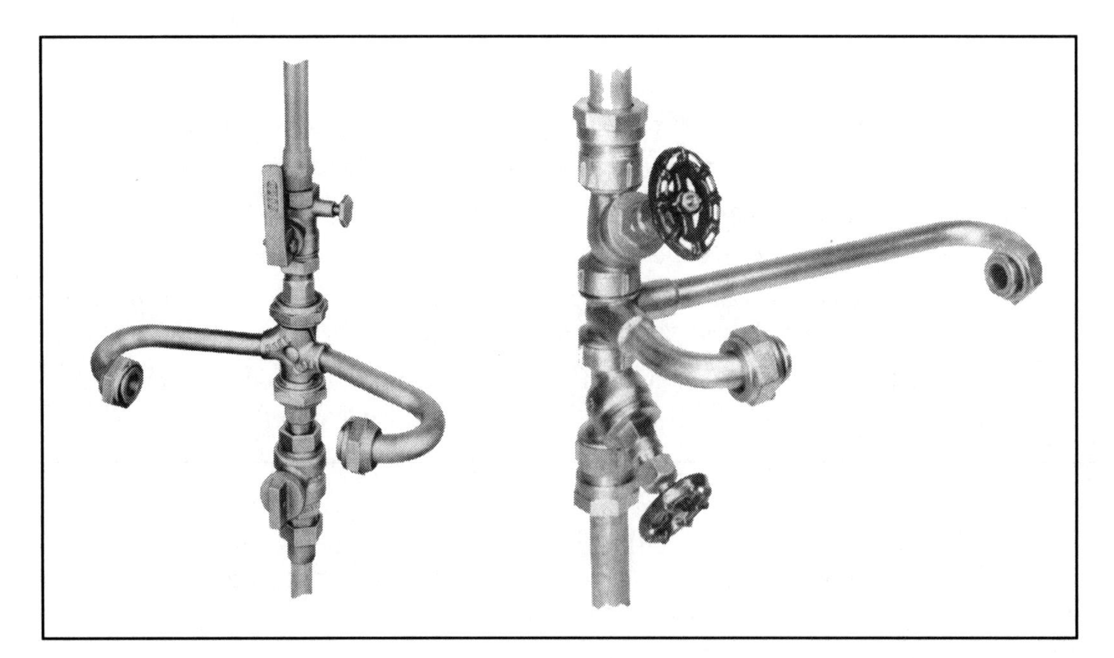

Figure 4-1 Two types of meter setters for vertical indoor piping

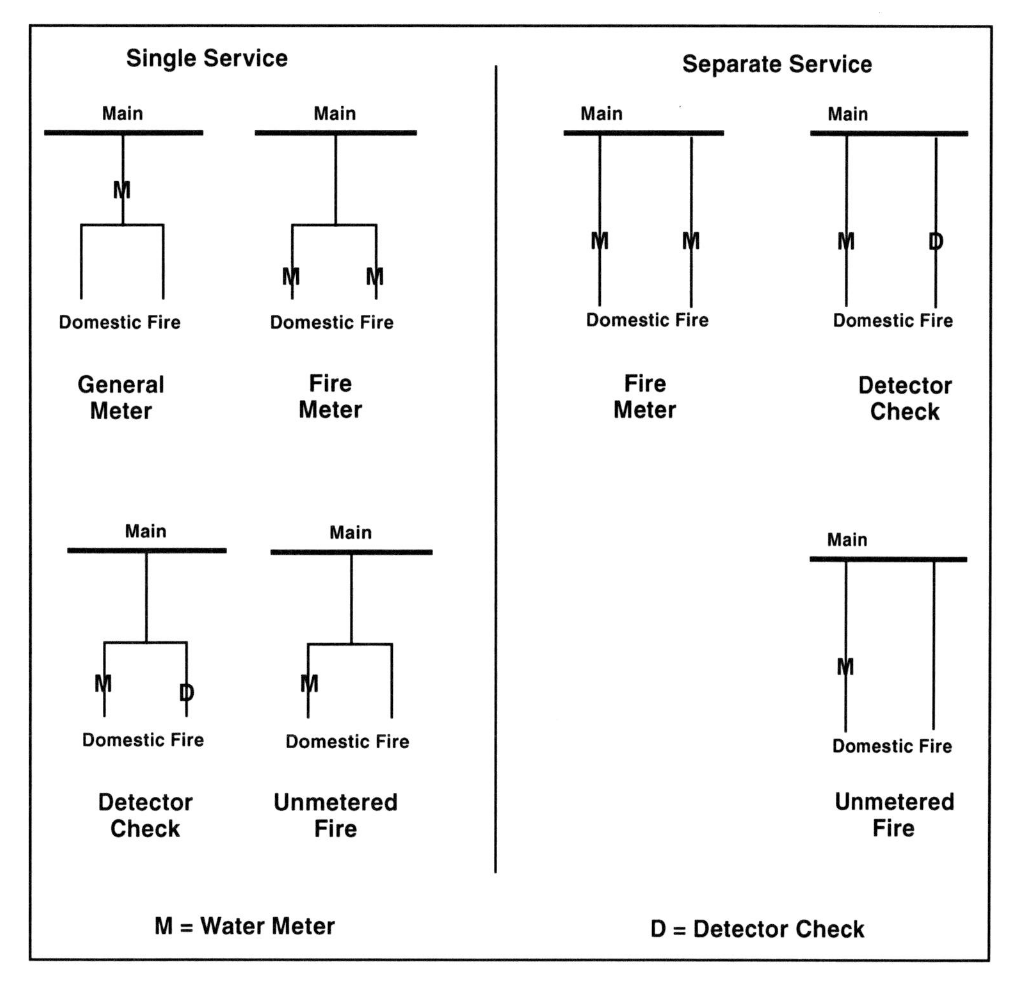

Figure 4-2 Meter arrangements for fire services. This figure is a representation of some possible meter arrangements for residential fire service. (Per NFPA 13D, the preferable arrangement would be bottom row, second from left.)

Courtesy: MARS Company

Figure 4-3 Residential fire service fitting

Indoor Settings

The installation of a small meter in a basement or utility room is a relatively simple job. Improper and unsatisfactory settings do occur, however, because of the absence of applicable standards. When indoor meters are to be read directly, a drawing should be made showing basic installation requirements. This drawing should include minimum and maximum elevations above the floor, the type of recommended connections, required valving, and minimum access space required for reading and service. The drawing should specify that the meter is to be located in the supply line as near as practicable to the point where it enters the basement or building. If a holding device is not used, the drawing should require an electrical ground connection across the meter. All settings should comply with local codes.

This standard drawing should be furnished to applicants for service, and compliance with the drawing should be one of the conditions for the utility's agreement to serve the premises. This type of drawing provides assurance of uniformly proper installation for the mutual benefit of the utility and the customer.

Outdoor Settings

Many factors influence the design, materials, installation details, and overall performance of an outdoor water-meter installation. Considerations include soil conditions, groundwater level, maximum frost penetration, and accessibility for ease of reading and service. Regardless of pit depth, the meter itself should be located at a depth from the surface that makes reading and accessibility convenient. It is also important to provide 2 in. (50 mm) to 4 in. (100 mm) of clearance between the service piping and the bottom of the meter pit to avoid any damage or strain that may occur if the meter box settles after installation. Consideration should also be given to the location of the curb stop or service control valve. This valve may be made an integral part of the meter setting or may be located elsewhere and housed in a separate curb box. Figure 4-4 illustrates good outdoor meter-setting practice.

The wide variation in ground frost penetration throughout the country makes it impossible to detail a universally practical outdoor setting. In areas where frost penetration is more than a few inches, serious consideration for frost protection is required. Knowledge of local conditions is necessary to select a pit of sufficient size and depth to provide frost protection. Differences in rate of frost penetration, depending on soil conditions, add considerable complications to this problem. Experience with outdoor installations under a given set of conditions is the best guide for avoiding freezing problems. Suggestions for meter pit design, including recommended size and depth, can be obtained from meter-box manufacturers.

Once sufficient experience has been established for meter-setting standards, it is recommended that a drawing be prepared as a guide for further meter settings. This drawing should specify (1) that the meter pit be located as close as possible to the utility line, which is the point of customer delivery; (2) that the lid of the pit or box be placed flush with the ground surface; (3) that no portion of the riser piping or meter be less than 1 in. (25 mm) to 2 in. (50 mm) from any portion of the meter box (more if required for frost protection); (4) the distance belowground surface where the meter spuds or couplings are to be located; (5) the dimensions of the meter box to be used for each size meter; and (6) the location of the curb stop or service-control valve.

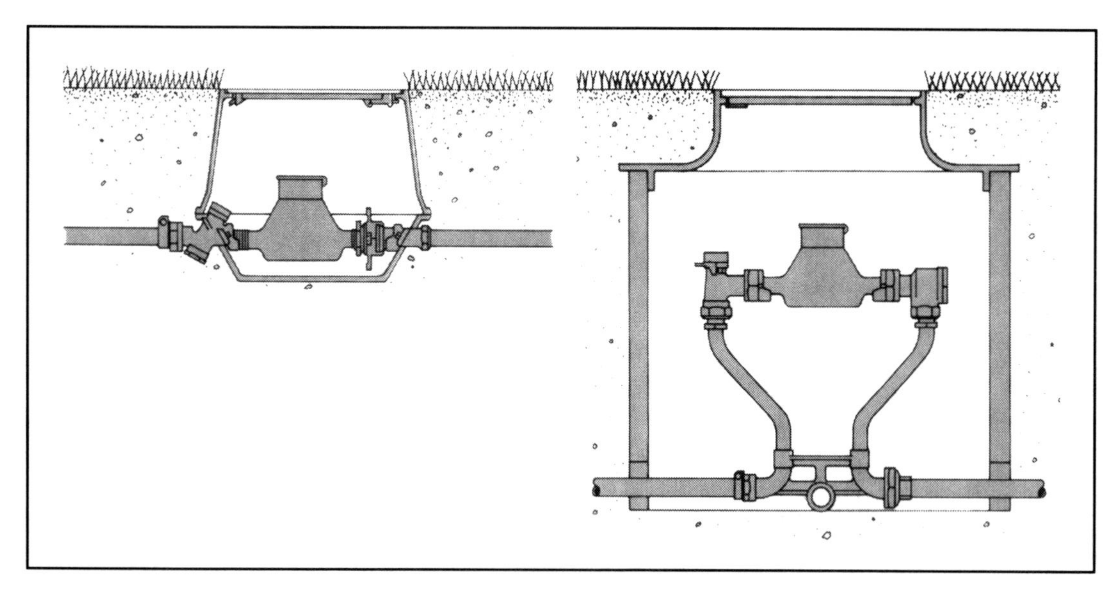

Figure 4-4 Outdoor meter settings with integral yoke (left) and meter yoke (right)

Large Meter Settings

Large meter settings, although made less frequently than small meter settings, are relatively expensive and require considerable preliminary planning. Large meters are heavy, and removal for service or testing can be costly and time-consuming. Provisions for fire service must also be given serious consideration.

Some utilities have adopted the practice of installing meters in manifolds of two equal branches with meters one size smaller than the main line. These installations consist of compound, turbine, multijet, or positive displacement meters. Caution should be exercised to ensure both branches contain meters of the same size, type, model, and manufacturer so that the water flow is balanced and performance life of the meters is equal. A manifold installation provides assurance of continuous service, because a metered, alternative water flow is available during maintenance or emergency situations. Figure 4-5 shows examples of 3-meter and 2-meter manifold installations using good installation practice and fire-service provisions.

If a manifold contains two or more branches or if meters are of different types or sizes, the installation requires considerable care in its design. Flow-regulating valves (not shutoff valves) are required for pressure loss adjustments to ensure proper water distribution through the various branches. The meter manufacturers or other engineering experts on hydraulics must be consulted because of the technical issues involved.

Check valves may be necessary in some manifolds to prevent recirculation or to improve the low-flow registration accuracy of the manifold system. Use of check valves requires careful consideration and should be designed by a professional.

To determine minimum distance to install subject fittings from class I and/or II turbine meters, compound meters, and fire-service meters, multiply the nominal pipe diameter of the installation by the appropriate number found in Table 4-1.

Custom-built meter setting devices in 1½-in. (40-mm) and 2-in. (50-mm) sizes with built-in bypass systems and valves with locking arrangements are now available. These devices offer a uniformity of meter settings, facilitate meter maintenance, and save space in a typical installation.

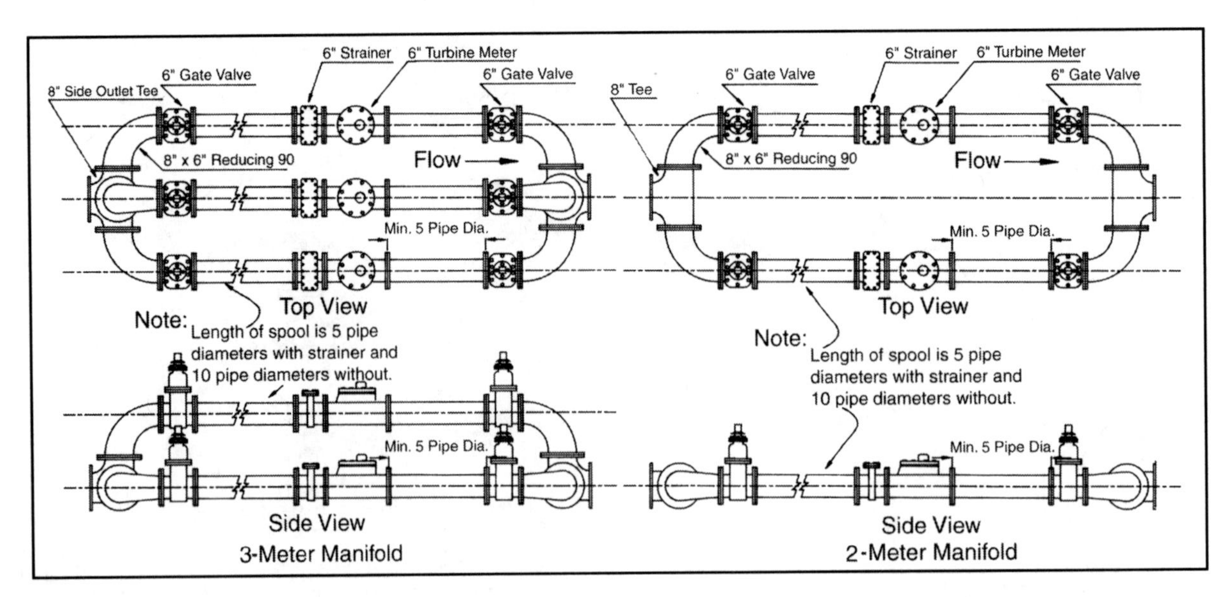

Typical 3-meter and 2-meter hydraulically balanced manifold.

Figure 4-5 Manifold of large meters

Table 4-1 Large meter installation guides for compound meters and class I and II turbine meters

Types of Fittings	Distance Upstream in Pipe Diameters	Distance Downstream in Pipe Diameters
Tees and crosses	10	5
Elbows and reducers	10	5
Tees and crosses with strainer or straighteners upstream	5	5
Elbows and reducers with strainer or straighteners upstream	5	5
Angle strainer	5	3
Basket strainer	5	3
Gate valve	1 to 3	1 to 3
Butterfly valve	5	5
Plug valve	5	5
Check valve	*	5
Pressure regulator	*	5
Test tee and plug	*	3
Saddle	*	3

* These fittings are not recommended for use upstream of a water meter. Under extreme high pressures, when it is necessary to protect the meter, pressure regulators may be considered for upstream use only after consulting with the meter manufacturer.

Many utilities prefer single-unit installations for large meters and find them very satisfactory. When a single large meter is installed, a bypass circuit should be provided so that meter maintenance can be accomplished without service interruptions. When large meters are installed in a vault, provision should be made for at least 20 in. (500 mm) of clearance to the vertical vault walls and at least 24 in. (600 mm) of head space from the highest point on the meter to the vault cover. Also, when a large meter installation is planned, it is essential that practical testing requirements be carefully considered in the meter and vault layout. Test valves should be installed to permit volumetric field tests, and provisions should be made for discharging test water.

The size, type, and meter brand may have a variety of size test ports for field testing. If the test port provided on the water meter is not adequate to produce the desired test flow, downstream test tees should be incorporated into the installation.

Satisfactory large meter settings can be designed in a variety of ways, depending on specific requirements, code specifications, and individual preferences. When manifolds are used, it is important to make sure each line is hydraulically the same in the manifold. However, it should be noted that these settings represent sizable investments that will provide long and satisfactory service if adequate planning is done in advance. Valuable advice and installation recommendations can be obtained by contacting the meter manufacturers; this advice should be sought in the preliminary planning stages of a new or unusual installation.

Class I or Class II Turbine-Meter Compound and Fire Service Installations

For optimum life and best accuracy, velocity meters work efficiently when there is a swirl-free, uniform-flow-velocity profile in the pipe immediately upstream of the meter. Because turbine meters are velocity meters, certain precautions or good practices are recommended, including the following.

Class I and class II turbine compound and fire service meters should be positioned horizontally. Piping should be arranged to ensure the meter remains full of water at all times and under a positive head. Elbows, reducers, tees, and crosses installed without a strainer upstream from the meter should be no closer than 10 pipe diameters of straight pipe of the same nominal diameter on the meter upstream and five diameters downstream. As a result of their increased flow capacity, smaller turbine meters are often used to replace larger-sized meters of other types. When pipe reducers are required in such cases, it is important that only gradual or tapered concentric reducers be used. Care should be exercised that the piping flange gaskets are centered and not protruding into the main flow stream.

Avoid installing check valves or pressure-regulating devices upstream of the meter. When check valves or pressure-regulating devices are required in the piping system, they should be installed downstream of the meter at a minimum of five pipe diameters. When backflow prevention devices are required, they should be installed downstream at a minimum of five pipe diameters. Full-opening ball or gate valves are preferred for the meter set's isolation valves. Butterfly or plug valves may also be used as isolation valves, if they are located at a minimum of five pipe diameters upstream and downstream of the meter. If the piping system requires a throttling valve, it should always be downstream of the meter at a minimum of five pipe diameters. It is recommended that a bypass arrangement (either permanent or temporary) be provided to permit uninterrupted customer service during periodic testing or routine maintenance in single-set meter installations. Flushing the lines any time a new installation has occurred or when maintenance has been performed on the line is recommended. To facilitate periodic testing, provision should be made for a test tee or plug at a minimum of three pipe diameters downstream of the meter.

A rigid flat-plate, Z-plate, or V-shaped strainer is recommended to protect the turbine metering element from debris carried in the flow stream. The effective open area of the strainer element should be at least twice the open pipe area of the meter inlet. When angle or regular basket strainers are used, they should be installed at a minimum of five pipe diameters upstream. When the piping system is also used for fire service, only a Factory Mutual Laboratories (FM)-approved or Underwriters Laboratories (UL)-listed meter should be used. Some meters require approved fire-service strainers as part of the metering package. Fire-service-rated strainers must be installed upstream of the meter.

When the piping installation, by necessity, creates a flow swirl in the upstream piping, a flow straightener should be used. At least two types are available: one type incorporates a concentric tube bundle, and the other uses a system of vanes. Either type of straightener can be installed integrally in the meter or immediately upstream. If a flow straightener is not used, the run of straight pipe immediately upstream of the meter should be increased at a minimum of 10 pipe diameters.

Caution should be exercised to avoid entrained air in the meter piping. This is most critical during meter startup when large slugs of entrained air could cause damage to the meter's internal measuring mechanism. Slowly filling the meter piping with a small bleed valve is good practice with the upstream isolation valve open and the downstream isolation valve closed. If possible, the small air-bleed valve should be located at a high point in the surrounding meter piping. The test opening, if valved, is used for this function.

The installation guidelines described are considered good practices for any meter installation and are repeated again in this section because of their importance in turbine meter installations. Figure 4-6 illustrates many of the suggested installation criteria for class I and class II turbine meters.

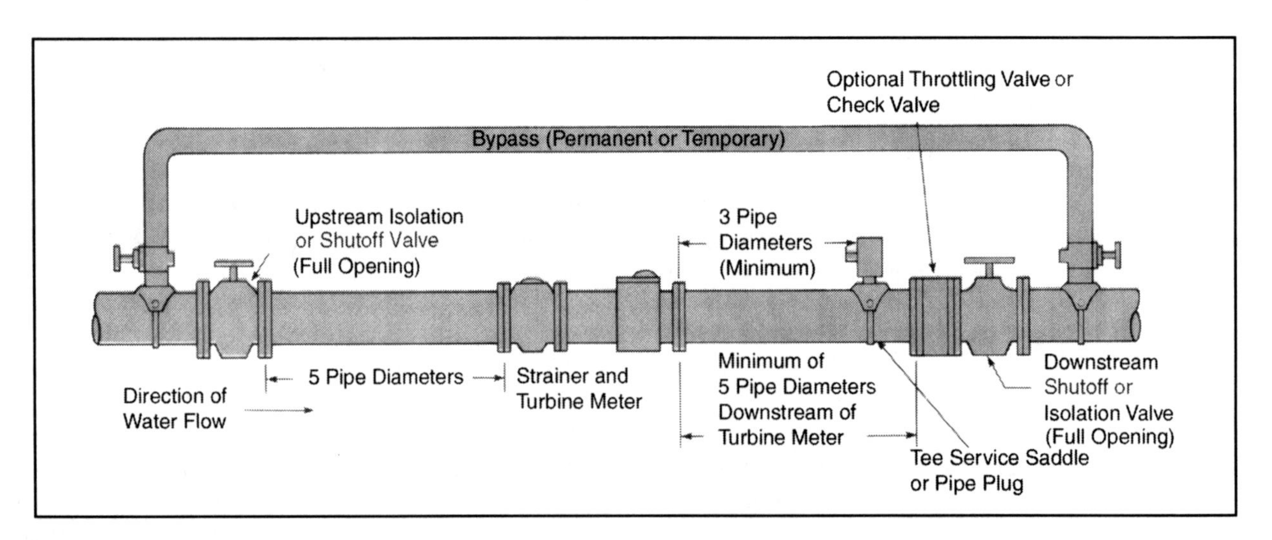

Figure 4-6 Optimum turbine meter installation

This page intentionally blank.

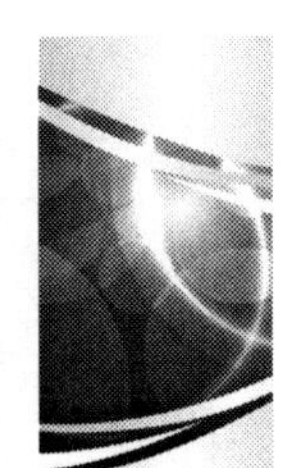

Chapter 5

Testing of Meters—Test Procedures and Equipment

INTRODUCTION

A water meter, like any other mechanical device, is subject to wear and deterioration and, over a period of time, loses its peak efficiency. How long water meters retain their overall accuracy depends on many factors, such as the quality of the water being measured, rates of flow and total quantity, and chemical buildup and abrasive materials carried by the water. The only way to determine whether a specific meter is operating efficiently is to test it. Establishing a meter maintenance program used to be very difficult, as it involves repetitive testing. Recent introduction of modern testing equipment reduces testing time and improves accuracy. From the individual customer's viewpoint, meters should be tested to protect the customer against meter inaccuracy that could result in overcharges from over-registration. This matter is also of concern to utility management. Experience shows, however, that the greater concern of a water utility should be the inequities and revenue loss that result from under-registration of meters.

The economic advantage of meter maintenance programs has been recorded in many articles, but most of these programs have represented concentrated efforts to rehabilitate meters after a long period of nonmaintenance. These programs are of little value in answering the question of how often meters should be tested. Unfortunately, there can be no single answer, as the economic result depends on factors such as rates charged for water; the effects of waters of different qualities on meters; and the cost of removing, testing, repairing, and installing meters. A proper economic balance should be attained. If meters are not adequately maintained, the utility loses revenue. Conversely, if the cost of a meter maintenance program is more than the loss of revenue incurred if the meters were not tested, the overall result is economic waste, and the utility's customers incur the unnecessary expense. Because modern water meters are technically more advanced than those that were produced just a few years ago, meters of today may no longer be disposable. Electronic registers and AMR systems are too valuable to throw away or ignore maintenance.

ACCURACY LIMITS

Accuracy limits are established to ensure that water meters record as accurately as possible. Meters have an inherent variation of 2 to 3 percent in registration over the entire range of flows. As an example, a ⅝-in. (15-mm) water meter in good condition will register within the following limits: 95 percent or higher at ¼-gpm (0.06-m^3/h) flow, a rise to a maximum of 101.5 percent at 2 gpm (0.45 m^3/h) (usually 10 percent of rated meter capacity), and then a falling off on a flat curve to not less than 98.5 percent at 20 gpm (4.5 m^3/h). This is the rated meter capacity for a ⅝-in. (15-mm) meter (refer to Figure 5-1 for an illustration of a typical accuracy curve).

It may not be economically feasible to repair older meters to meet the accuracy requirements for new meters. The water utility should carefully weigh all costs to make a specific determination. For this reason, separate accuracy limits are shown in Table 5-3 for new, rebuilt, and repaired meters on the minimum flow test. The limits set for repaired meters represent those that require good meter-shop procedures. Meter repair work is not acceptable if repaired meters do not register at least 90 percent on this test. Older meters may not be repairable to modern standards or advanced register systems. A higher accuracy percentage is recommended for desirable shop-quality standards and may be a requirement of the state, provincial, or federal regulatory agencies.

In many cases, meter manufacturers have provided revenue-maintenance programs in the form of replacement measuring-chamber assemblies and modern register assemblies, wherein the accuracy of the repaired meter can be restored to the same level as that of a new meter. The reality is that most repaired meter standards are not acceptable to most modern utility meter shops due to the importance of revenue protection. The practice of repairing meters to new meter standards is becoming standard practice.

Determining Accuracy Limits for Meter Types

A weighted average meter accuracy can be calculated, based on accuracy test results at various flow rates and an assumed model for actual consumption patterns in the field. For example, one such weighting function for residual meter applications is the algebraic sum of 15 percent of the low flow results, 70 percent of the intermediate flow results, and 15 percent of the maximum flow results. For typical turbine-meter applications, a different weighting function such as 10 percent of the low flow results, 65 percent of the intermediate flow results, and 25 percent of the maximum flow results might be used. For compound and fire-service compound-type meters, the weighted average meter accuracy might be one-third of the algebraic sum of the accuracy results at the maximum test-flow rate of the main-line meter and the maximum and intermediate test-flow rates of the bypass meter.

Accuracy Limits for Removal From Service

Meters with unacceptable accuracies (as defined by regulatory agencies or by internal concerns over unaccounted-for water or revenue losses) should be repaired or replaced. Table 5-1 provides an example of recommended accuracy limits. Determining the optimum number of years a meter should remain in service between tests is achieved by testing 5 percent of those meters next scheduled or past due for periodic testing under

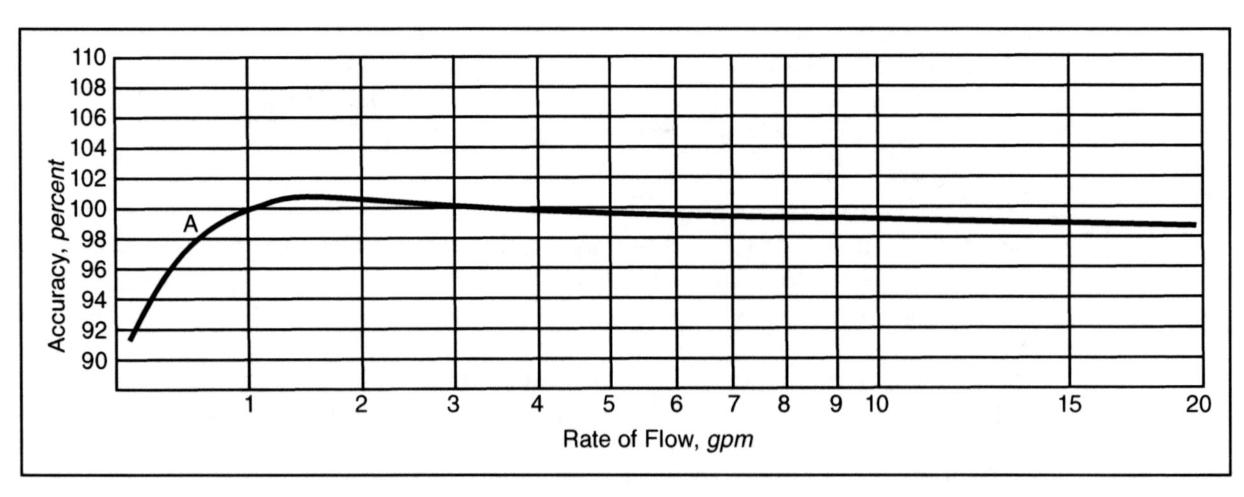

Highest registration occurs at approximately 7 to 10 percent of maximum capacity.

Figure 5-1 A typical accuracy curve for a ⅝-in. (15-mm) meter

an existing testing schedule. If the results of these tests fall within the accuracies shown in Table 5-1, it is assumed that the remaining meters will produce the same average test results. This procedure should be followed each year until the test results indicate that a longer time interval between tests would still produce results compliant with the accuracy limits in Table 5-1. At this time, the remaining meters should be removed and tested as part of the periodic test program. At this point the optimum number of years for periodic testing can be determined. As long as all factors remain unchanged, it can be assumed that the periodic testing period will remain constant. Table 5-2 contains testing intervals for many states. A more aggressive program can result in significant annual savings.

Statistical sample testing in a meter distribution system is an alternative method for determining the optimum number of years a meter should remain in service, especially residential meters ⅝ in. (15 mm) through 1 in. (25 mm) in size. Sample testing is a cost-effective management approach to determine the variables affecting meter performance and to monitor the overall accuracy of the metering system. Using established statistical methods, a random selection of meters determined by the year the meter was installed will provide data on the entire metering system. Weighting the statistical sample information with the system demand information determines the service-life decision.

The sample-test database, sorted by the purchase year and by the consumption rate, can be used to identify or window groups of meters with similar accuracy problems. This information will be used as a criteria to select changeout based on performance rather than age or type. Maintenance programs are an excellent opportunity to upgrade meters with new technology. This ensures that the money used to exchange meters is spent on the poorest performing meters within the system.

Calibration

The information in this section is provided for historical purposes, as mechanical-drive meters with gear-train technology are no longer manufactured.

In a mechanical-drive meter and in many magnetic-drive meters, the gear train includes two changeable gears allowing the ratio between the motion of the measuring element and the register to be adjusted for maximum accuracy of registration. Changed gears are no substitute for good meter-repair standards. Gearing changes

Table 5-1 Accuracy limits for compliance with guidelines

Meter Type (all sizes)	Accuracy Limits as Found by Testing *percent*	
	Normal Test Flow Rates	Minimum Test Flow Rates
Displacement	96–102	90–102
Multijet	96–102	90–104
Singlejet	96–102	90–104
Fluidic oscillator	96–102	90–102
Propeller and turbine	96–103	Not applicable
Compound and fire service	95–104	Not applicable

should be based on tests made at the high point on the performance curve to ensure that the meter registers near optimum accuracy.

The following description demonstrates how the displacement of water in the measuring chamber is transmitted to the meter register and converted to standard units of measure. Although the maximum speed of ⅝-in. (15-mm) meters is limited to 435 piston revolutions or nutations/ft^3 (15,400 rev/m^3) by 1995 AWWA standards, most meters have measuring speeds considerably below this maximum. Furthermore, meters are manufactured with three to five gear-reduction stages. In the example that follows, a composite figure of element's speed of 310 nutations/ft^3 (10,950 rev/m^3) is used in combination with a four-gear reduction train.

The volume of the measuring-chamber assembly of this composite meter is, therefore, approximately 1/310 ft^3, and 310 revolutions of the disc spindle are required to cause the smallest hand of the meter register to make one complete revolution and record 1 ft^3.

The intermediate gear train consists of four sets of reduction pinions and gears; each driving pinion has seven teeth and each driven gear has 28 teeth. The meter design (or trial) gears for registration in cubic feet consists of a driver gear with 24 teeth and a driven gear with 29 teeth.

In any gear train, the change in speed is the product of the number of teeth of the driver gears divided by the number of teeth of the driven gears. Therefore, in this meter, the reduction of the 310 revolutions of the disc spindle to one revolution of the 1-ft^3 index of the register is done as follows:

$$310 \times \frac{7}{28} \times \frac{7}{28} \times \frac{7}{28} \times \frac{7}{28} \times \frac{24}{29} = \frac{7{,}440}{7{,}424}$$

$$= 100.215\% \text{ (Curve A in Figure 5-1)}$$

This same meter geared for registration in gallons requires only a different set of change gears. For example, if a 24-tooth driver gear and 39-tooth driven gear are used, and the number of revolutions of the disc spindle are increased from 310 to 413⅓, an increase of one third, as 10 gal equals 1.3368 ft^3, then

$$413\frac{1}{3} \times \frac{7}{28} \times \frac{7}{28} \times \frac{7}{28} \times \frac{7}{28} \times \frac{24}{39} = \frac{9{,}920}{9{,}984}$$

$$= 99.359\%$$

Thus, the smallest index of the meter register records 10 gal for each complete revolution.

These examples show that one basic design is used for meters recording in various units of measure by mere substitution of the change gears and register dial plate. This feature is of value from a production cost standpoint but is not the only reason for changing gears. These gears are also used to compensate for differences in meter accuracy resulting from manufacturing tolerances, wear, or other service conditions.

Multijet Meters—Calibration Device

Contrary to the positive-displacement meters, where the ratio between the register and the measuring chamber is changed mechanically, in some multijet meters, changes are made hydraulically, whereas in other multijet designs, the accuracy can be adjusted mechanically.

In some models, calibration is done by a variable-port regulating device incorporated along an internal bypass channel in the meter. Usually the device will be in the form of a screw, accessible from the outside without the need to disassemble the meter or the register and protected by a sealed plug.

Turbine Meters—Calibration Device

Some turbine meter designs have an adjusting vane that can be used for a simple hydraulic calibration. Adjustment is done with a screwdriver. Changing the position of the adjusting vane will affect the entire accuracy curve, but it might not shift the whole curve by the same amount.

TESTING NEW METERS

All new meters should be tested for accuracy of registration at flow rates and test-flow quantities in accordance with Table 5-3 before they are placed in service. This procedure ensures the water utility that the new meter is accurate and that a complete history is available when the meter is eventually brought back to the maintenance shop for inspection or maintenance, or if a customer challenges the meter's accuracy.

During the procurement process, specifications that require the manufacturer to provide certified meter test results are advantageous. Certified test results may easily be transferred to a database thus establishing the complete history of a meter. The database can be referenced for inspection or maintenance work, or to address customer concerns. A statistical sample testing of new meter shipments to verify accuracy and to maintain confidence in manufacturer test results is an efficient cost alternative to testing every new meter.

Program Coordination

To start a program of periodic testing, it is necessary to set an arbitrary time in which to complete the work. Also, it is desirable to select a period of years that coincides with the best estimate of the frequency with which meters should be tested. In this way, the work load is leveled out, and approximately the same number of meters will be due for testing each time. If, for example, a utility with 10,000 meters in service sets up a program for testing meters on a 10-year cycle, the utility has to remove approximately 900 meters each year. This amount is less than 10 percent of the number in service, as there are always meters that will not remain in service for the full period but will be removed for other reasons.

In order to provide for even work flow, both in the changing of meters and the shop work, the number of orders required should be prepared on a daily basis. Assuming

250 working days in a year, in order to complete the periodic testing of 900 meters per year, the testing of approximately four meters each day would be necessary in addition to other required work. If, therefore, four orders are written each day, the progress of the program may be reviewed at any time by a count of the number of incomplete orders for changing meters for periodic test and a check to see if the shop work is completed without a backlog of meters.

Although the testing of 10,000 meters may seem a staggering job, it is surprising that once the work is started on a systematic basis, the additional work is absorbed and soon becomes routine. As actual test results of meters removed from service are accumulated, experience is obtained as to how long it takes, on the average, for meters to lose sensitivity on the low flows. The length of time meters are permitted to remain in service can be adjusted on the basis of known results.

Large Meters

It is generally considered advisable to provide for more frequent testing of large meters, because an error in their registration affects revenue to a much greater extent. Furthermore, current and compound meters may under- or over-register to a much greater degree than positive-displacement meters.

If enough 3-in. (80-mm) and larger meters are installed, the repair and testing of these larger meters may be delegated to one particular person or crew. They will develop special skills that are necessary for the effective maintenance of larger meters. A survey of the largest utilities in the United States determined that the testing period for the larger meters is conducted on a yearly basis. However, the surprisingly large variation in test periods indicates a need for close study of this important policy. In any meter-testing program, accurate and readily available records are essential. A formal, ongoing meter record program should be established as an initial step in the program. Electronic data processing has proven to be a highly effective tool in maintaining an effective meter record program.

When any testing program is considered, some general observations are pertinent. An initial service period should be assumed, whether it is 30, 25, 20 years, or less. Older meters and those carrying the heaviest volume should be given priority, because volume measured is definitely related to meter wear. Magnetic-drive meters should have a longer maintenance period than mechanical-drive meters.

Probably the best advice that can be given regarding a meter testing program is to be alert to and study all phases of the metering field; there is no substitute for experience in determining the best procedure for any one utility. Although a metered system is the best known for equitably spreading the cost of water service, serious inequities and injustices can occur unless all meters are maintained at a high, uniform level of efficiency and unless every reasonable effort is made to prevent inequities from occurring.

Test Procedures

No phase of water-utility operation has been handled in so many different ways as the testing of water meters. The closest approach to standard test procedures has been the accuracy requirements contained in the AWWA meter standards and AWWA Manual M6, and these have been widely used as a basis for establishing individual testing methods. With the exception of specific rates set forth for testing meters on a minimum flow, the specifications make no provision for the number of different rates of flow on which meters should be tested; what these various rates of flow should be; or the quantities of water to be used in running such tests. It is understandable that the meter specifications do not contain these provisions, as the accuracy requirements are primarily a warranty to the buyer that meters purchased in accordance with the specifications will register within certain accuracy limits. The confusion and wide variance in testing procedures result from the fact that the testing of water meters in ordinary shop practice is primarily concerned with meters that are not new but that have been removed from service and repaired. Each individual has had to begin with the information available and develop testing procedures. Under such circumstances, it is not difficult to understand the reason for the widely divergent procedures that have developed over the years, many of which do not produce reasonable answers on overall operational ability of the meters tested.

Although many state regulatory commissions have adopted regulations concerning frequency of meter tests, it should be noted that any arbitrary time interval applied to several localities, each with its own unique local conditions, is not economically feasible for all. Table 5-2, compiled in 1995 and showing data as of 1994, lists these regulations. It must be recognized, however, that the very existence of such regulations has often resulted in better maintenance of meters. It is inexplicable why meter maintenance is, in too many instances, considered of secondary importance. Only when meters are formally recognized as the only means by which revenue is equitably obtained to operate the water system will the necessary time and study be given to the question of how often it is necessary to test meters for the most efficient and economic results.

Table 5-3 includes recommended data for testing cold-water meters by the use of the volumetric method, using volumetric tanks, or the gravimetric method, using weight scales. Accuracy standards for new meters are contained in the latest editions of the following AWWA standards: C700, C701, C702, C703, C704, C708, C710, C712, and C713.

The primary reason for meter tests is to ensure that the cost of water service is equitably distributed among all customers. Unless all meters register within defined limits of accuracy, equitable cost distribution does not occur. For this reason, regulatory commissions have established definitive meter-accuracy requirements and the frequency of tests for water meters. A review of such commission requirements indicates that each agency varies slightly in test frequencies, so it is important to be familiar with local regulations.

In addition, loss of revenue to the water utility will occur if the meters are not maintained efficiently. Unfortunately, meters may under-register for long periods without complete stoppage. It is necessary to test meters periodically to minimize this loss of revenue. The accuracy of displacement meters, inferential meters, multijet or current meters, is also subject to change while they are in service, and they may either under- or over-register. The period of time for which water meters retain overall accuracy is variable and depends on the characteristics, quality, and volume of the water being measured. The rates charged for water service also have a distinct bearing on how frequently meters should be tested. It is difficult to determine the economic balance between the cost of more frequent testing and potential loss in revenue caused by meter under-registration. Proper meter tests are necessary, however, in any such evaluation. Unless meter-testing procedures reflect overall operational ability and the same procedures are followed consistently, changes in meter accuracy after periods of service cannot be determined.

Finally, it would be advantageous if everyone spoke the same language. Many seminars are held annually on meter department operation and test procedures, but no common ground can be found for comparison unless the results are based on one method or standard.

Table 5-2 State public service commission regulations for periodic testing of water meters as of Nov. 30, 1994*

			Meter Size in. (mm)								Meter Size in. (mm)				
			⅝ (15)	¾ (20)	1 (25)	1½ (40)	2 (50)	3 (80)	4 (100)	6 or larger (150)	⅝ (15)	¾ (20)	1 (25)	1½ (40)	2 (50)
State	Effective Year	Rule Number	Interval Between Tests *Years*								Registration Between Tests *1,000 ft³* (28me)				
Alabama	(2)	W-17	10	8	6	4	4	3	2	1					
Alaska	1986	6.02	10	8	6	4	4	4	4	4	200	300	400		
Arizona (1)															
Arkansas															
California (3)	1967	103	20	20	15	10	10	10	10	10					
Colorado†	1949	21	5	5	5	4	4	3	2	1					
Connecticut	1966	16-11-88	8	8	8	4	4	3	2	1					
Delaware	1980	2076	15	15	10	10	3	3	3	1					
Florida															
Georgia (1)															
Hawaii															
Idaho (1)															
Illinois	1975	I.A.C.83 Part 600	6	6	4	4	4	4	4	4	100	300	300		
Indiana	1988	170 LAC 6-1	10	10	8	6	4	4	4	4	100	150	300		
Iowa (4)	1986	21.6(10)													
Kansas (1)															
Kentucky	1992	KAR 5:066	10	10	10	4	4	2	1	1					
Louisiana (1)															
Maine (3)	1987	Chap. 620	8	8	8	6	6	4	2	1	100	150	300		
Maryland	1968	6.9.2	10	8	6	4	4	2	2	1					
Massachusetts (1)															
Michigan (5)	1963	R460.13601	10	8	6						100	150	300		
Minnesota (1)															
Mississippi (1)															
Missouri	1968	42	10	6	4	4	4	4	4	4	200	300	400		
Montana	(2)	9	10	10	10	10	10	10	10	10					
Nebraska (1)															
Nevada (1)															
New Hampshire (2)		605.04(6)	10	10	4	4	4	2	1	1					
New Jersey	(2)	14:9-3.2	10	8	6	4	4	4	4	4	750	1,000 (6)	2,000 (6)		
New Mexico (1)															

(continued)

Table 5-2 State public service commission regulations for periodic testing of water meters as of Nov. 30, 1994* (continued)

			Meter Size *in. (mm)*								Meter Size *in. (mm)*				
			⅝ (15)	¾ (20)	1 (25)	1½ (40)	2 (50)	3 (80)	4 (100)	6 or larger (150)	⅝ (15)	¾ (20)	1 (25)	1½ (40)	2 (50)
State	Effective Year	Rule Number	Interval Between Tests *Years*								Registration Between Tests *1,000 ft^3* (28me)				
New York	1981	16 NYCRR Part 500.1	15	15	5	4	4	3	2	1	1,500 (6)	2,000 (6)	2,000 (6)	3,000 (6)	7,000 (6)
North Carolina (7)	1952	R7-32				4	4	3	2	1					
North Dakota (1)															
Ohio (4)	1991	4901:1-15-21													
Oklahoma (4)	1971	165:65-7-11	10	10	10	6	6	4	2	2					
Oregon (1)															
Pennsylvania	1963	7	10	8	6	4	4	4	4	4	100	150	300		
Rhode Island	1966	Schedule	10	10	10	10	10	2	1	1					
South Carolina (1)															
South Dakota (1)															
Tennessee (8)	(2)														
Texas (1)															
Utah†	1937	R746-300-3													
Vermont															
Virginia (1)															
Washington	1971	480-110-161	10	8	6	4	4	2	2	2					
West Virginia	1948	38	7	7	5	4	4	2	1	1					
Wisconsin (4)	1994	PSC 185	10	10	10	4	4	2	2	1					
Wyoming	1979	Sec. 608	10	8	6	4	4	4	4	4	100	150	300		

* Data are condensed for simplification. Detailed or specific current information should be obtained from the state regulatory agency. Testing intervals included in this tabulation are statutory and are not recommended periods.

† No response was received from current survey. Data from old survey are included in table.

(1) No regulations for periodic testing having been adopted.

(2) Effective date not furnished.

(3) A utility may submit a different periodic test plan for meters to the commission for approval.

(4) As often as necessary to comply with commission accuracy standards.

(5) Meters larger than 1 in. (25 mm) should be tested following recommendations in AWWA standards.

(6) Registration is in units of 1,000 gal.

(7) Applies only to compound, velocity, and fire-line meters.

(8) Each utility sets its own schedule.

Elements of a Meter Test

Accuracy denotes the comparison between a meter's indicated quantity of water passing through it as compared to the actual quantity of water passing through it as determined by the test system, or proving system. In the water industry, the meter's accuracy is most commonly called the *percent registration* (% registration). A water meter that has 101% accuracy, or a percent registration of 101%, at a given flow rate indicates that 1% more water is registered on the meter than is actually delivered (this error is called 1% fast); in this case, the meter over-registers by 1%. Conversely, a meter that has 99% accuracy indicates that 1% less water is registered on the meter than is actually delivered (i.e., 1% slow); the meter under-registers by 1%.

Flow range is the maximum, intermediate, and minimum flow rates established by the manufacturer of the meter being tested and closely represented by the flow rates listed in Table 5-3. The range is sometimes expressed as a ratio where the maximum flow rate is compared to the minimum flow rate. A meter capable of being accurate from 20 gpm (4.5 m^3/h) to 200 gpm (45 m^3/h) would have a 10:1 flow range as an example.

A meter's characteristic accuracy curve (also called a performance curve) is a continuous curve drawn between all accuracy points over the meter's flow range. Most water meter manufacturers' literature contains a performance curve for their particular meter model. Generally speaking, all meters of the same general type (disc, piston, multijet, compound, or turbine) will exhibit the same or similar characteristic accuracy curve.

Accuracy Issues

Repeatability is the measure of deviation of a series of accuracy tests from the test's mean value where all of these accuracy tests were conducted under exactly identical conditions. This term can be applied to either the test system or the meter under test.

Precision usually refers to the combined sources of all errors in a test system, which may include data presentation and operator interpretation errors as well as the combined proving system repeatability errors of each component. In addition to these sources of error, a test system might have a bias where the test system indicated proof quantity is displaced from the true value at one or all proof quantities.

The following are the three basic elements of a meter test:

1. The number of different rates of flow over the operating range of a meter required to determine overall meter efficiency.
2. The quantities of water necessary at the various test rates to provide reasonable resolution of meter registration accuracy.
3. Accuracy limits that meters must meet on the different rates to be acceptable for use.

Test Rates

The three rates of flow necessary to properly test displacement, compound, propeller, and other types of water meters are maximum, intermediate, and minimum. At least one additional test, preferably more, is necessary within the changeover range of flows of compound and fire-service meters to determine overall operational efficiency and accuracy of registration.

Table 5-3 Test requirements for new, rebuilt, and repaired cold–water meters*

Displacement Meters (AWWA C700 and C710)

Size	Maximum Rate (All Meters)				Intermediate Rate (All Meters)				Minimum Rate (New and Rebuilt)				Minimum (Repaired)
	Flow Rate†	Test Quantity††		Accuracy Limits	Flow Rate**	Test Quantity††		Accuracy Limits	Flow Rate	Test Quantity††		Accuracy Limits	Accuracy Limits
in.	*gpm*	*gal*	*ft^3*	*percent*	*gpm*	*gal*	*ft^3*	*percent*	*gpm*	*gal*	*ft^3*	*percent*	*percent (min)*
½	8	100	10	98.5–101.5	2	10	1	98.5–101.5	¼	10	1	95–101	90
½ × ¾	8	100	10	98.5–101.5	2	10	1	98.5–101.5	¼	10	1	95–101	90
⅝	15	100	10	98.5–101.5	2	10	1	98.5–101.5	¼	10	1	95–101	90
⅝ × ¾	15	100	10	98.5–101.5	2	10	1	98.5–101.5	¼	10	1	95–101	90
¾	25	100	10	98.5–101.5	3	10	1	98.5–101.5	½	10	1	95–101	90
1	40	100	10	98.5–101.5	4	10	1	98.5–101.5	¾	10	1	95–101	90
1½	50	100	10	98.5–101.5	8	100	10	98.5–101.5	1½	100	10	95–101	90
2	100	100	10	98.5–101.5	15	100	10	98.5–101.5	2	100	10	95–101	90

Multijet Meters (AWWA C708)

Size	Maximum Rate (All Meters)				Intermediate Rate (All Meters)				Minimum Rate (New and Rebuilt)				Minimum (Repaired)
	Flow Rate†	Test Quantity††		Accuracy Limits	Flow Rate**	Test Quantity††		Accuracy Limits	Flow Rate	Test Quantity††		Accuracy Limits	Accuracy Limits
in.	*gpm*	*gal*	*ft^3*	*percent*	*gpm*	*gal*	*ft^3*	*percent*	*gpm*	*gal*	*ft^3*	*percent*	*percent (min)*
⅝	15	100	10	98.5–101.5	1	10	1	98.5–101.5	¼	10	1	97–103	90
⅝ × ¾	15	100	10	98.5–101.5	1	10	1	98.5–101.5	¼	10	1	97–103	90
¾	25	100	10	98.5–101.5	2	10	1	98.5–101.5	½	10	1	97–103	90
1	35	100	10	98.5–101.5	3	10	1	98.5–101.5	¾	10	1	97–103	90
1½	70	100	10	98.5–101.5	5	100	10	98.5–101.5	1½	100	10	97–103	90
2	100	100	10	98.5–101.5	8	100	10	98.5–101.5	2	100	10	97–103	90

Singlejet Meters (AWWA C712)

Size	Maximum Rate (All Meters)				Intermediate Rate (All Meters)				Minimum Rate (New and Rebuilt)				Minimum (Repaired)
	Flow Rate†	Test Quantity††		Accuracy Limits	Flow Rate**	Test Quantity††		Accuracy Limits	Flow Rate	Test Quantity††		Accuracy Limits	Accuracy Limits
in.	*gpm*	*gal*	*ft^3*	*percent*	*gpm*	*gal*	*ft^3*	*percent*	*gpm*	*gal*	*ft^3*	*percent*	*percent (min)*
⅝	15	100	10	98.5–101.5	2	10	1	98.5–101.5	¼	10	1	95–101.5	90
⅝ × ¾	15	100	10	98.5–101.5	2	10	1	98.5–101.5	¼	10	1	95–101.5	90
¾	25	100	10	98.5–101.5	3	10	1	98.5–101.5	½	10	1	95–101.5	90
1	40	100	10	98.5–101.5	4	10	1	98.5–101.5	¾	10	1	95–101.5	90
1½	50	100	10	98.5–101.5	8	100	10	98.5–101.5	½	100	10	95–101.5	90
2	100	100	10	98.5–101.5	15	100	10	98.5–101.5	½	100	10	95–101.5	90
3	160	500	50	98.5–101.5	20	100	10	98.5–101.5	½	100	10	95–101.5	90
4	250	500	50	98.5–101.5	40	100	10	98.5–101.5	¾	100	10	95–101.5	90
6	500	1,000	100	98.5–101.5	60	100	10	98.5–101.5	1½	100	10	95–101.5	90

Fluidic-Oscillator Meters (AWWA C713)

Size	Maximum Rate (All Meters)				Intermediate Rate (All Meters)				Minimum Rate (New and Rebuilt)				Minimum (Repaired)
	Flow Rate†	Test Quantity††		Accuracy Limits	Flow Rate**	Test Quantity††		Accuracy Limits	Flow Rate	Test Quantity††		Accuracy Limits	Accuracy Limits
in.	*gpm*	*gal*	*ft^3*	*percent*	*gpm*	*gal*	*ft^3*	*percent*	*gpm*	*gal*	*ft^3*	*percent*	*percent (min)*
½	8	100	10	98.5–101.5	2	10	1	98.5–101.5	¼	10	1	95–101	90
½ × ¾	8	100	10	98.5–101.5	2	10	1	98.5–101.5	¼	10	1	95–101	90
⅝	15	100	10	98.5–101.5	2	10	1	98.5–101.5	¼	10	1	95–101	90
⅝ × ¾	15	100	10	98.5–101.5	2	10	1	98.5–101.5	¼	10	1	95–101	90

(continued)

Table 5-3 Test requirements for new, rebuilt, and repaired cold-water meters* (continued)

Fluidic–Oscillator Meters (AWWA C713)														
¾	25	100	10	98.5–101.5	3	10	1	98.5–101.5	½	10	1	95–101	90
1	40	100	10	98.5–101.5	4	10	1	98.5–101.5	¾	10	1	95–101	90
1½	50	100	10	98.5–101.5	8	100	10	98.5–101.5	1½	100	10	95–101	90
2	100	100	10	98.5–101.5	15	100	10	98.5–101.5	2	100	10	95–101	90

Class I Turbine Meters, Vertical–Shaft Type (AWWA C701)

	Maximum Rate (All Meters)				Intermediate Rate (All Meters)				Minimum Rate (New and Rebuilt)				Minimum (Repaired)
Size	Flow Rate†	Test Quantity††		Accuracy Limits	Flow Rate**	Test Quantity††		Accuracy Limits	Flow Rate	Test Quantity††		Accuracy Limits	Accuracy Limits
in.	*gpm*	*gal*	*ft³*	*percent*	*gpm*	*gal*	*ft³*	*percent*	*gpm*	*gal*	*ft³*	*percent*	*percent (min)*
¾	30	100	10	98–102	3	10	1	98–102	1½	10	1	98–102	--
1	50	100	10	98–102	5	10	1	98–102	2	10	1	98–102	--
1½	100	500	50	98–102	10	100	10	98–102	3	100	10	98–102	--
2	160	500	50	98–102	16	100	10	98–102	4	100	10	98–102	--
3	350	1,000	100	98–102	35	100	10	98–102	6	100	10	98–102	--
4	600	1,500	200	98–102	60	100	10	98–102	8	100	10	98–102	--
6	1,250	4,000	500	98–102	125	1,000	100	98–102	15	1,000	100	98–102	--

Class II Turbine Meters, In-Line (High-Velocity) Type (AWWA C701)

	Maximum Rate (All Meters)				Intermediate Rate (All Meters)				Minimum Rate (New and Rebuilt)				Minimum (Repaired)
Size	Flow Rate†	Test Quantity††		Accuracy Limits	Flow Rate**	Test Quantity††		Accuracy Limits	Flow Rate	Test Quantity††		Accuracy Limits	Accuracy Limits
in.	*gpm*	*gal*	*ft³*	*percent*	*gpm*	*gal*	*ft³*	*percent*	*gpm*	*gal*	*ft³*	*percent*	*percent (min)*
1½	100	500	50	98.5–101.5					4	100	10	98.5–101.5	--
2	160	500	50	98.5–101.5					4	100	10	98.5–101.5	--
3	350	1,000	100	98.5–101.5					8	100	10	98.5–101.5	--
4	630	1,500	200	98.5–101.5					15	100	10	98.5–101.5	--
6	1,400	4,000	500	98.5–101.5					30	1,000	100	98.5–101.5	--
8	2,400	7,000	900	98.5–101.5					50	1,000	100	98.5–101.5	--
10	3,800	10,000	1,300	98.5–101.5					75	1,000	100	98.5–101.5	--
12	5,000	15,000	2,000	98.5–101.5					120	1,000	100	98.5–101.5	--
16	10,000	30,000	4,000	98.5–101.5					200	1,000	100	98.5–101.5	--
20	15,000	40,000	5,000	98.5–101.5					300	1,000	100	98.5–101.5	--

Propeller Meters (AWWA C704)

	Maximum Rate (All Meters)				Intermediate Rate (All Meters)				Minimum Rate (New and Rebuilt)				Minimum (Repaired)
Size	Flow Rate†	Test Quantity††		Accuracy Limits	Flow Rate**	Test Quantity††		Accuracy Limits	Flow Rate	Test Quantity††		Accuracy Limits	Accuracy Limits
in.	*gpm*	*gal*	*ft³*	*percent*	*gpm*	*gal*	*ft³*	*percent*	*gpm*	*gal*	*ft³*	*percent*	*percent (min)*
2	100	300	40	98–102					35	200	25	98–102	90
3	250	800	100	98–102					40	200	25	98–102	90
4	500	1,500	200	98–102					50	250	30	98–102	90
6	1,200	2,500	300	98–102					90	500	60	98–102	90
8	1,500	3,000	400	98–102					100	500	60	98–102	90
10	2,000	4,000	500	98–102					125	500	60	98–102	90
12	2,800	6,000	800	98–102					150	750	100	98–102	90
14	3,750	8,000	1,000	98–102					250	1,000	130	98–102	90
16	4,750	10,000	1,300	98–102					350	1,500	200	98–102	90
18	5,625	12,000	1,600	98–102					450	2,000	250	98–102	90
20	6,875	15,000	2,000	98–102					550	2,500	300	98–102	90
24	10,000	20,000	2,500	98–102					800	4,000	500	98–102	90
30	15,000	30,000	4,000	98–102					1,200	6,000	800	98–102	90
36	20,000	40,000	5,000	98–102					1,500	7,500	1,000	98–102	90

(continued)

Table 5-3 Test requirements for new, rebuilt, and repaired cold-water meters* (continued)

Propeller Meters (AWWA C704)

42	28,000	40,000	5,000	98–102	2,000	10,000	1,300	98–102	90
48	35,000	50,000	6,000	98–102	2,500	12,500	1,500	98–102	90
54	45,000	60,000	8,000	98–102	3,200	16,000	2,000	98–102	90
60	60,000	70,000	9,000	98–102	4,000	20,000	2,500	98–102	90
66	75,000	80,000	11,000	98–102	4,750	25,000	3,000	98–102	90
72	90,000	90,000	12,000	98–102	5,500	28,000	3,500	98–102	90

Compound Meters (AWWA C702)§

	Maximum Rate (All Meters)					Change Over Point (All Meters)				Minimum Rate (New and Rebuilt)				Minimum (Repaired)
Size	Flow Rate†	Test Quantity††		Accuracy Limits		Flow Rate**	Test Quantity††		Accuracy Limits	Flow Rate	Test Quantity††		Accuracy Limits	Accuracy Limits
in.	*gpm*	*gal*	*ft³*	*percent*		*gpm*	*gal*	*ft³*	*percent*	*gpm*	*gal*	*ft³*	*percent*	*percent (min)*
				Class I	Class II									
2	160	400	50	97–103	98.5–101.5				90–103				95–101	90
3	320	1,000	100	97–103	98.5–101.5				90–103				95–101	90
4	500	1,500	200	97–103	98.5–101.5				90–103				95–101	90
6	1,000	3,000	400	97–103	98.5–101.5				90–103				95–101	90
8	1,600	4,000	500	97–103	98.5–101.5				90–103				95–101	90
10	2,300	4,000	500	97–103	98.5–101.5				90–103				95–101	90

Fire–Service Type, Type I and Type II (AWWA C703)
(Test at intermediate rate not necessary.)§

	Maximum Rate (All Meters)					Change Over Point (All Meters)				Minimum Rate (New and Rebuilt)				Minimum (Repaired)
Size	Flow Rate†	Test Quantity††		Accuracy Limits		Flow Rate**	Test Quantity††		Accuracy Limits	Flow Rate	Test Quantity††		Accuracy Limits	Accuracy Limits
in.	*gpm*	*gal*	*ft³*	*percent*		*gpm*	*gal*	*ft³*	*percent*	*gpm*	*gal*	*ft³*	*percent*	*percent (min)*
				Type I	Type II									
3	350	700	100	97–103	98.5–101.5									90
4	700	1,500	200	97–103	98.5–101.5				Not less than 85%				Not less than 95%	90
6	1,600	3,000	400	97–103	98.5–101.5									90
8	2,800	5,000	700	97–103	98.5–101.5									90
10	4,400	9,000	1,200	97–103	98.5–101.5									90

Fire Service Type, Type III (AWWA C703)

	Maximum Rate (All Meters)				Intermediate Rate (All Meters)				Minimum Rate (New and Rebuilt)				Minimum (Repaired)
Size	Flow Rate†	Test Quantity††		Accuracy Limits	Flow Rate**	Test Quantity††		Accuracy Limits	Flow Rate	Test Quantity††		Accuracy Limits	Accuracy Limits
in.	*gpm*	*gal*	*ft³*	*percent*	*gpm*	*gal*	*ft³*	*percent*	*gpm*	*gal*	*ft³*	*percent*	*percent (min)*
3	350	700	100	98.5–101.5	10	100	10	98.5–101.5	4	100	10	95–101.5	--
4	700	1,500	200	98.5–101.5	30	500	50	98.5–101.5	10	100	10	95–101.5	--
6	1,600	3,000	400	98.5–101.5	60	1000	100	98.5–101.5	20	1000	100	95–101.5	--
8	2,800	5,000	700	98.5–101.5	70	1000	100	98.5–101.5	30	1000	100	95–101.5	--
10	4,400	9,000	1,200	98.5–101.5	110	1000	100	98.5–101.5	35	1000	100	95–101.5	--

* A rebuilt meter is one that has had the measuring element replaced with a factory–made new unit. A repaired meter is one that has had the old measuring element cleaned and refurbished in a utility repair shop.

† These are suggested test flows and test quantities. Testing for high rates of flow can be achieved by testing the meter at 25% of the meters rating if the manufacturer's original test certificate indicates a linear curve between 25% and 100% of the rated flow range.

†† Quantity should be one or more full revolutions of the test hand but not less than 3 min running. When limited test capabilities force the use of smaller test quantities, the resultant increase in total test uncertainties and errors need to be recognized when establishing acceptance criteria tolerance.

§ The bypass meter should be tested in accordance with the appropriate test requirements for the type of meter used.

** As this rate varies according to manufacturer, it should be determined for each type of meter tested.

Metric Conversions: in. × 25.4 = mm, gal × 0.003785 = m^3, gpm × 0.2268 = m^3/h, ft^3 × 0.02831 = m^3.

Tests for full-flow accuracy do not need to be made at the "safe maximum capacity" rate shown in the applicable AWWA standard. Registration curves of water meters show that meters in good operating condition follow a general pattern of registration. The specific profile of the accuracy curve can be different for each type of meter. Usually, there will be an intermediate point of maximum registration above the low-flow-metering zone. Depending on the size and type of meter, this point may vary between 3 to 10 percent of the rated meter capacity. At rates above that of maximum registration, the accuracy curve is fairly flat so that there is little difference in accuracy over a wide range of flows. Selection of the maximum rate of flow at which meters are tested is, therefore, not of major importance. Maximum-rate test flows of 25 percent or more, if desired by the owner, of rated capacity are practical, because meters are seldom operated at rated capacity. This lower test rate is advantageous with multiple testing of small meters and is possible with pressures and testing equipment usually available.

The intermediate rate of flow should be at or near the high point of registration to ensure against over-registration of the meter on any rate of flow and, therefore, should be approximately 10 percent of rated capacity. The minimum-rate-flow test discloses operational ability and proficiency of meter repair more than either the maximum- or intermediate-flow tests. All three, however, are necessary to evaluate overall meter accuracy. Test rates of flows should be measured in actual units, such as gallons per minute. Rates based on size of orifice are not reliable because of possible enlargement of the orifice from wear or changes in pressure in the supply line.

Test Quantities

The quantity of water required to provide acceptable accuracy depends on the accuracy and resolution of the test equipment, as well as the desired accuracy of the test results. Commercial calibrated tanks with visually adjustable read height scales can provide overall equipment error of less than 0.25 percent if the scale reading error is small compared to the final height of the collected water. Measuring tanks based on weight, referred to as the gravimetric method, can provide even higher accuracy (e.g., 0.10 percent) using class II or class III precision scales and load cells. In both systems, the use of digital equipment can reduce instrument reading error to zero and improve overall system accuracy.

Test Requirements

When choosing the quantity of water to be collected for any test, refer to Table 5-3 of this manual or the applicable AWWA standard for the meter type being tested.

Where large quantities of water are used for testing large meters, it is more expedient to employ gravimetric means involving the use of computers and electronics with load cells. These procedures make possible testing "on the fly," thereby eliminating the effects of valve opening and closing, particularly at high flows, and allow adequate test accuracy even with compressed test quantities, as long as adequate reading resolution is possible for the meter under test.

Table 5-4 is intended for ascertaining the percentage of true quantity indicated by the meter, when the meter is run for a measured tank volume of 20, 30, 40, 50, or 60 gal.

It must be stressed that the test volumes associated with the various meter sizes, types, and flow rates indicated in Table 5-3 be followed to minimize measurement system error. Compressed volumetric testing at lesser volumes can result in significant errors and is not recommended.

Table 5-4 Percentage registration tables for test quantities other than 10, 100, or 1,000 gal or ft³

Meter Reading *ft³ or gal*	Percent of Actual Volume	Meter Reading *ft³ or gal*	Percent of Actual Volume	Meter Reading *ft³ or gal*	Percent of Actual Volume	Meter Reading *ft³ or gal*	Percent of Actual Volume	Meter Reading *ft³ or gal*	Percent of Actual Volume
19.0	95.0	29.0	96.6	39.0	97.5	49.0	98.0	59.0	98.3
1	95.5	1	97.0	1	97.7	1	98.2	1	98.5
2	96.0	2	97.3	2	98.0	2	98.4	2	98.6
3	96.5	3	97.6	3	98.2	3	98.6	3	98.8
4	97.0	4	98.0	4	98.5	4	98.8	4	99.0
5	97.5	5	98.3	5	98.7	5	99.0	5	99.1
6	98.0	6	98.6	6	99.0	6	99.2	6	99.3
7	98.5	7	99.0	7	99.2	7	99.4	7	99.5
8	99.0	8	99.3	8	99.5	8	99.6	8	99.6
19.9	99.5	9	99.6	9	99.7	9	99.8	9	99.8
				Actual Volume*					
20.0	100.0	30.0	100.0	40.0	100.0	50.0	100.0	60.0	100.0
1	100.5	1	100.3	1	100.2	1	100.2	1	100.1
2	101.0	2	100.6	2	100.5	2	100.4	2	100.3
3	101.5	3	101.0	3	100.7	3	100.6	3	100.5
4	102.0	4	101.3	4	101.0	4	100.8	4	100.6
5	102.5	5	101.6	5	101.2	5	101.0	5	100.8
6	103.0	6	102.0	6	101.5	6	101.2	6	101.0
7	103.5	7	102.3	7	101.7	7	101.4	7	101.1
8	104.0	8	102.6	8	102.0	8	101.6	8	101.3
20.9	104.5	9	103.0	9	102.2	9	101.8	9	101.5
21.0	105.0	31.0	103.3	41.0	102.5	51.0	102.0	61.0	101.6

* For 100 division dial, move decimal one place to right.

Metric Conversion: gal × 0.003785 = m³.

Using automated gravimetric testing equipment, however, with its inherent greater accuracy, allows the operator to use much smaller quantities and still obtain good accuracy in determining the actual water volume that has passed through the meter under test. (The limiting factor in total test error may then be in the reading resolution available for the volume indicated by the meter under test.) All scales and calibrated tanks should be tested and certified to acceptable commercial tolerances. Scales and their calibration procedures are in NIST* Handbook 44 for weighing systems.

Testing Interval

Ongoing meter-testing programs have long been advocated by AWWA and are required by most public utility commissions and other regulatory agencies (see Table 5-2). It is in the best interest of both the utility and the customer that testing of meters be part of an ongoing maintenance program.

The chemical and physical characteristics of water are the most important factors affecting the performance of a meter. Because the characteristics of water vary throughout the country, an arbitrary number of years is not the criterion to use for determining the length of time between tests. From an economic standpoint, a meter should remain in service until it ceases to register within accepted accuracy limits. Because meter testing programs are costly, prudent management for revenue protection dictates that meters should be left in service as long as practical. Because of these

* National Institute of Standards and Technology, 100 Bureau Dr., Gaithersburg, MD 20899.

variable factors, it is recommended that a utility's own test results be used to determine the length of time its meters should remain in service between tests. The utility may also consider using test intervals that are recommended for use in their area.

The following guidelines were established so that a utility could establish its own periodic meter-test intervals based on its historical data. The guidelines are designed to be flexible so that different test intervals may be established for different types of meters or for different manufacturers' meters. Time intervals may even be established for new meters that differ from those for repaired meters. Different time intervals may also be established for meters in areas supplied with water from different sources if those sources result in water-quality variances.

Meters will be considered to be in compliance with these guidelines if both of the following conditions are met:

1. Ninety-five percent of the meters scheduled for tests on a periodic basis are actually tested. (It must be recognized that 100 percent of the meters scheduled for test cannot always be tested through no fault of operational procedures.)

2. At least 95 percent of the meters actually tested register results within the accuracy limits shown in Table 5-1 for both normal and minimum test-flow rates. These accuracy limits are determined prior to any adjustment or repair of the meter after it has been in service for a period of time. Only meters tested in conjunction with the periodic testing program should be used in computing average periodic accuracy results.

Statistical Sample Testing

Sample testing is an alternative method to evaluate the performance and service life of a cross section of meters. In addition to providing insight into variables affecting meter performance, this method also allows the utility to monitor the overall accuracy of its meters. Sampling is a useful management tool in addressing metering activities, as well as identifying problems with specific meters.

Most utilities' metering programs involve a changeout policy once a meter has reached a certain age or predetermined life expectancy. These programs assume that all newly purchased meters perform better than the older meters in the system. If this assumption is wrong then the utility may be exchanging meters that are more accurate than those remaining, therefore producing a loss of revenue. Statistical sample testing identifies the poorest-performing meters and allows the utility to exchange meters based on performance.

Statistical data is used and accepted throughout the business world as an excellent tool for making informed management decisions. Information developed from sample testing will provide the utility with data in which trend analysis can be made and performance levels for specific meters can be identified.

The first steps to implement a sample testing program are to understand and identify the established statistical methods. This may be accomplished through educational training or by referencing basic statistical methods in textbooks.

After developing a basic understanding of statistical sampling, the following steps should be implemented:

1. Determine desired confidence level.

2. Determine appropriate sample lot size for the confidence level.

3. Determine criteria for testing (size, age, volume, type).

4. Randomly select and retrieve.
5. Test and document.
6. Analyze test data.
7. Report with recommendations.

The following is an example that identifies the benefits of sample testing and performance-based meter changeouts versus annual changeout based on age. In this example, a 95 percent confidence level is achieved. The appropriate lot size to achieve a 95 percent confidence level was determined to be a minimum of 5 percent of the total meters for a particular set year, regardless of total population size. The criteria used in this example to sample test meters was the year in which the meter was put in service, "set year." A minimum of 5 percent of the meters from each sample lot (set year) is randomly pulled from field service and is returned to the meter test facility for shop testing.

Testing standards identified in this manual should be followed and adhered to. Extreme care should be used when retrieving and testing sample metering to best duplicate field accuracy/conditions. The example data includes an overall weighted average determined by assigning weights of 15 percent–70 percent–15 percent to the low, intermediate, and high test results, respectively.*

Based on established statistical methods, reports such as Table 5-5 can be developed from the sample data. If these data were used to exchange meters based on performance, the meters set in 1992 would be scheduled for exchange. If the exchange criteria were based on age, the utility would exchange meters more accurate than others in the system, therefore not being cost effective.

Although confidence levels are lost, the sample data can be queried by purchase year (Table 5-6) and by consumption (Table 5-7). Reviewing the data in different ways will identify the group or type of meters that are least accurate. In Table 5-6, purchase year 1992 is again identified as the least accurate group of meters in the sample data.

Statistical testing is a management tool. As utility managers strive to make good management decisions, data to assist the decision making is essential. Statistical testing provides the data to make cost-effective management decisions.

Test Equipment

Equipment required to test a water meter may be very simple (Figure 5-2). A rotameter is a useful flow-measuring device for precise control in meter testing. It consists of a tapered, calibrated glass tube in which a stainless-steel rotor is free to move up and down in the center of the tube, guided by a stainless-steel guide. The instrument is positioned above a flow-regulating valve. Water passing up the tapered tube raises the rotor to a stable position. The rate of flow is read across the top of the rotor on a scale of figures etched in the body of the glass tube. Rotameters are commercially available for meter-repair-shop testing apparatus. Figure 5-3 illustrates basic features of a rotameter.

At high flow rates, modern scale systems have built-in buffers that are programmable to eliminate the effect of impact and vibrations and produce accurate flow data. While scale systems can also deliver average flow data for the entire duration of the test, good operating practice suggests comparing those values with the actual timed flow rates for verification of the built-in buffers. Under "quiet" discharge conditions

---

* Statistical sampling technique for controlling the accuracy of small water meters. Penchih Tao. *Journal AWWA*. June 1982.

Table 5-5 1999 sample test meters test results—set date

Set Date	Flow Rates: Low	Flow Rates: Intermediate	Flow Rates: High	Overall Weighted Average
1998	94.72	100.63	90.30	99.54
1997	97.66	100.90	99.63	100.22
1996	86.27	100.98	99.58	98.56
1995	88.86	100.68	98.97	98.65
1994	72.11	100.08	98.61	95.61
1993	79.34	100.02	97.95	96.61
1992	70.09	98.83	98.28	94.43
1991	71.76	100.34	98.82	95.83
1990	71.70	101.03	99.59	96.43
1989	86.20	100.96	99.43	98.52
1988	78.84	100.93	99.68	97.43
1987	88.85	99.90	99.68	98.21
1986	89.07	98.88	99.11	97.44
1985	82.24	100.50	99.46	97.61
1984	90.35	101.24	99.66	99.37
1983	89.50	101.38	99.94	98.38

		Slow Meters (accuracy below 98.5 percent)				Accurate Meters (accuracy 98.5-101.5 percent)				Fast Meters (accuracy above 101.5 percent)				Entire Population	
Set Year	Number of Meters Tested	Number of Meters	Percentage of Total	Average	Standard Deviation	Number of Meters	Percentage of Total	Average	Standard Deviation	Number of Meters	Percentage of Total	Average	Standard Deviation	Average	Standard Deviation
98	79	3	3.80	83.38	1.78	76	96.20	100.18	0.51	0	0.00	0.00	0.00	99.54	3.27
97	79	1	1.27	84.07	0.00	78	98.73	100.43	0.51	0	0.00	0.00	0.00	100.22	1.90
96	79	12	15.19	88.18	5.56	66	83.54	100.38	0.51	1	1.27	103.15	0.00	98.56	4.93
95	77	13	16.88	91.12	6.13	64	83.12	100.18	0.63	0	0.00	0.00	0.00	98.65	4.27
94	77	31	40.26	89.17	6.70	46	59.74	100.04	0.68	0	0.00	0.00	0.00	95.67	6.84
93	78	31	39.74	91.67	8.87	47	60.26	99.86	0.58	0	0.00	0.00	0.00	96.61	6.90
92	78	37	47.44	88.40	13.73	40	51.28	88.84	0.67	1	1.28	101.56	0.00	94.43	11.07
91	80	34	42.50	90.53	5.99	46	57.50	99.74	0.66	0	0.00	0.00	0.00	95.83	6.02
90	77	24	31.17	87.81	4.46	53	68.83	100.32	0.85	0	0.00	0.00	0.00	96.42	6.34
89	79	12	15.19	88.61	4.86	67	84.61	100.29	0.67	0	0.00	0.00	0.00	98.52	4.64
88	79	21	26.58	88.76	5.43	54	68.35	100.49	0.64	4	5.06	101.55	0.00	97.43	5.95
87	80	15	18.75	87.63	20.37	62	77.50	100.60	0.61	3	3.75	101.66	0.10	98.21	10.20
86	75	14	18.67	85.99	21.87	59	78.67	100.01	0.72	2	2.67	101.97	0.24	97.44	10.95
85	77	21	27.27	91.32	7.99	55	71.43	99.92	0.72	1	1.30	102.60	0.00	97.61	5.72
84	79	12	15.19	93.54	4.82	63	79.75	100.32	0.71	4	5.06	101.97	0.27	99.37	3.19
83	25	2	8.00	89.62	4.00	22	88.00	100.14	0.65	1	4.00	102.25	0.00	99.38	3.18

Total Number of Meters Tested—1,198
Total Number of Slow Meters—283 Percent of Total—24
Total Number of Accurate Meters—898 Percent of Total—75
Total Number of Fast Meters—17 Percent of Total—1

Sample ⅝ in. (15 mm) and ⅝ in. × ¾ in. (15 mm × 20 mm) meters by set year

Table 5-6 1999 sample test meters test results—purchase date

Set Date	Flow Rates Low	Flow Rates Intermediate	Flow Rates High	Overall Weighted Average
1998	95.93	100.59	99.36	99.71
1997	94.77	100.73	99.48	99.65
1996	94.21	100.98	99.70	99.77
1992	63.28	98.71	98.30	93.34
1991	77.91	100.52	98.59	96.84
1990	87.84	100.62	98.84	97.09
1989	78.82	101.03	99.49	97.61
1988	84.71	100.98	99.62	98.34
1987	88.41	99.98	99.71	98.21
1984	88.38	99.54	99.11	97.80
1983	91.41	101.13	99.72	99.46

		Slow Meters (accuracy below 98.5 percent)				Accurate Meters (accuracy 98.5-101.5 percent)				Fast Meters (accuracy above 101.5 percent)				Entire Population	
Purchase Year	Number of Meters Tested	Number of Meters	Percentage of Total	Average	Standard Deviation	Number of Meters	Percentage of Total	Average	Standard Deviation	Number of Meters	Percentage of Total	Average	Standard Deviation	Average	Standard Deviation
98	51	1	1.96	83.22	0.00	50	98.04	100.04	0.49	0	0.00	0.00	0.00	99.71	2.38
97	75	3	4.00	82.88	1.22	72	96.00	100.35	0.49	0	0.00	0.00	0.00	99.65	3.47
96	85	4	4.71	85.66	0.27	81	95.29	100.47	0.52	0	0.00	0.00	0.00	99.77	3.18
92	112	68	60.71	89.03	11.14	44	39.29	99.99	0.68	0	0.00	0.00	0.00	93.34	10.21
91	122	42	34.43	91.23	6.16	80	65.57	99.78	0.63	0	0.00	0.00	0.00	96.84	5.40
90	214	61	28.50	89.53	7.37	152	71.03	100.08	0.70	1	0.47	103.15	0.00	97.09	6.22
89	76	17	22.37	88.03	4.27	59	77.63	100.38	0.72	0	0.00	0.00	0.00	97.61	5.56
88	115	22	19.13	89.22	5.56	89	77.39	100.34	0.65	4	3.48	101.55	0.00	98.34	5.11
87	86	16	18.60	87.50	19.73	66	76.74	100.59	0.60	4	4.65	101.63	0.10	98.21	9.95
84	120	21	17.50	86.77	18.76	93	77.50	100.01	0.75	6	5.00	102.14	0.28	57.80	9.38
83	23	5	21.74	96.30	2.43	17	73.91	100.27	0.77	1	4.35	101.55	0.00	99.46	2.14

Total Number of Meters Tested—1,079
Total Number of Slow Meters—260 Percent of Total—24
Total Number of Accurate Meters—803 Percent of Total—74
Total Number of Fast Meters—16 Percent of Total—1

Sample ⅝ in. (15 mm) and ⅝ in. × ¾ in. (15 mm × 20 mm) meters by purchase year

Table 5-7 1999 sample test meters test results—consumption

	Per 1,000 Gallons Consumption	Flow Rates Low	Intermediate	High	Overall Weighted Average
01	0–100	89.42	100.36	98.87	98.50
02	100–200	86.03	100.81	99.31	98.37
03	200–300	86.79	100.70	99.22	97.49
04	300–400	78.81	99.72	99.12	98.49
05	400–500	79.61	100.47	99.01	97.13
06	500–600	81.18	99.43	99.03	96.63
07	600–700	72.75	100.73	99.25	96.31
08	700–800	87.02	100.87	99.28	98.55
09	800–900	84.56	101.02	99.25	98.28
10	900–1,000	81.88	100.08	99.40	97.67
11	1,000–1,100	83.87	98.73	99.40	96.60
12	1,100–1,200	80.61	100.88	99.38	97.61
13	1,200–1,300	89.58	101.35	99.48	99.31
14	1,300–1,400	89.58	101.19	99.22	100.04
15	1,400–1,500	96.36	101.00	99.22	97.67
16	1,500–1,600	87.41	99.53	99.26	97.67

		Slow Meters (accuracy below 98.5 percent)				Accurate Meters (accuracy 98.5-101.5 percent)				Fast Meters (accuracy above 101.5 percent)				Entire Population	
Cons. Rmg	Number of Meters Tested	Number of Meters	Percentage of Total	Average	Standard Deviation	Number of Meters	Percentage of Total	Average	Standard Deviation	Number of Meters	Percentage of Total	Average	Standard Deviation	Average	Standard Deviation
01	120	14	11.67	88.44	10.59	105	87.50	100.19	0.54	1	0.83	103.15	0.00	98.50	5.99
02	144	23	15.97	87.98	5.18	121	84.03	100.34	0.59	0	0.00	0.00	0.00	98.37	5.01
03	148	32	21.62	87.83	5.33	115	77.70	100.15	0.68	1	0.68	101.55	0.00	97.49	5.68
04	120	37	30.83	87.97	13.72	81	67.50	126.26	0.75	2	1.67	101.64	0.09	96.49	9.53
05	98	34	34.69	91.26	6.04	63	64.29	100.22	0.69	1	1.02	101.55	0.00	97.13	5.59
06	76	25	32.89	89.52	16.40	51	67.11	100.11	0.66	0	0.00	0.00	0.00	96.63	10.66
07	75	25	33.33	88.21	5.19	48	64.00	100.30	0.76	2	2.67	101.90	0.35	96.31	6.50
08	90	21	23.33	93.15	5.68	67	74.44	100.15	0.74	2	2.22	101.88	0.33	98.55	4.11
09	52	11	21.15	91.30	5.99	41	78.85	100.16	0.74	0	0.00	0.00	0.00	98.28	4.60
10	61	18	29.66	91.66	5.59	43	70.49	100.18	0.74	0	0.00	0.00	0.00	97.67	4.98
11	42	9	21.43	83.18	24.83	32	76.19	100.20	0.70	1	2.38	102.17	0.00	96.60	13.40
12	37	11	29.73	91.68	5.83	25	67.57	100.06	0.67	1	2.70	101.55	0.00	97.61	5.03
13	30	5	16.67	93.79	5.22	23	76.67	100.25	0.78	2	6.67	102.20	0.40	99.31	3.36
14	24	4	16.67	93.76	4.94	19	76.17	100.20	0.72	1	4.17	102.25	0.00	99.21	3.25
15	21	2	9.52	96.15	0.00	18	85.71	100.38	0.61	1	4.76	101.55	0.00	100.04	1.40
16	58	13	22.41	89.76	11.58	43	74.14	99.87	0.73	2	3.45	101.76	0.14	97.67	6.97

Total Number of Meters Tested—1,196

Total Number of Slow Meters—284   Percent of Total—24

Total Number of Accurate Meters—895   Percent of Total—75

Total Number of Fast Meters—17   Percent of Total—1

into a gravimetric tank, the rate of change in indicated tank weight can be used instead to measure the flow rate being delivered during the test.

If a large number of meters is to be tested, complete test equipment is commercially available. Also, the various meter-testing components may be purchased individually from commercial manufacturers, and an organization can fabricate its own test equipment for any particular application. Certified test equipment meeting approved national standards may be preferred because certified devices used by trained technicians "speaks directly to courts."

Meters may be tested singly or in groups, and the equipment selected should be based on the work load. When reasonable judgment is exercised in the selection of test equipment, the cost is quickly repaid and more accurate results are usually obtained. Requisites of a good meter test facility are:

- A test bench on which meters may be quickly and securely held
- An inlet valve
- A quick-closing valve on bench discharge and a flow-regulating valve
- A rate-of-flow indicator
- One or more tanks, preferably calibrated for volumetric testing, or a tank set on platform scales for testing by weight (calibrated tanks, of course, must be installed in a plumb position to avoid inaccuracies of calibration)
- Adequate lighting of test area
- Cabinets for systematic storage of change gears, hand tools, and records
- A recirculating system or an ample supply of water so that pressure will fluctuate as little as possible
- Convenient and accessible location, and carefully designed shop layout to increase efficiency

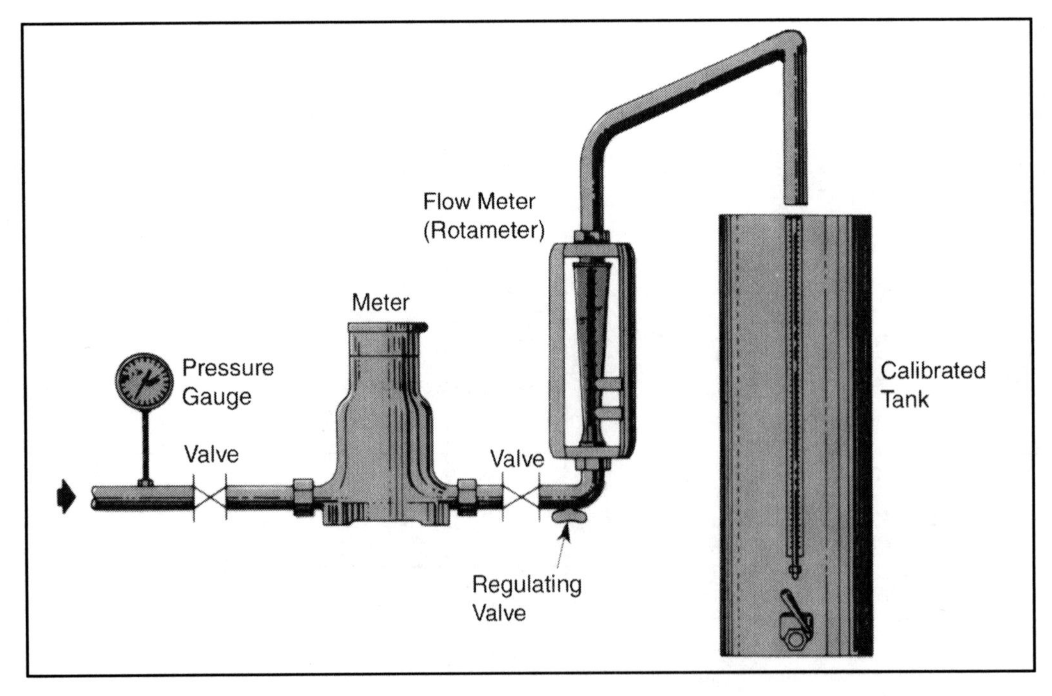

Figure 5-2 Basic requirements for a volumetric meter-testing assembly

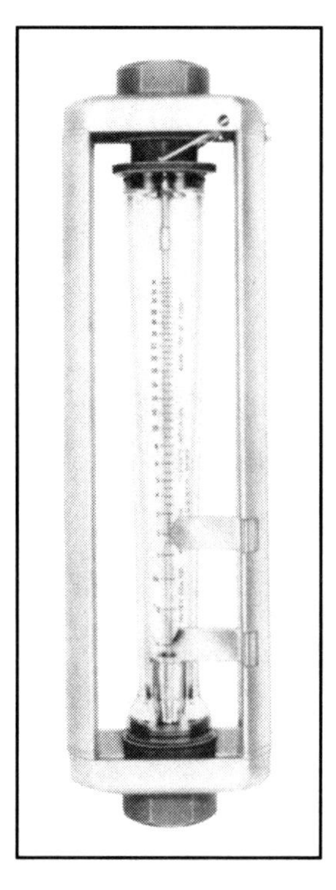

Figure 5-3 Rotameter rate-of-flow indicator

Safety is an important consideration because water in motion can be very dangerous. Certified equipment should be used for accuracy and technician safety.

Basic equipment for testing $\frac{5}{8}$-in. (15-mm), $\frac{3}{4}$-in (20-mm), and 1-in. (25-mm) meters consists of the following items:

- A 10-ft^3 or 100-gal (0.5-m^3) capacity tank, preferably calibrated for volumetric testing
- A 1-ft^3 or 10-gal (0.05-m^3) capacity tank, similarly equipped
- A test bench provided with necessary fittings, including a control inlet valve, a quick-acting rate control valve on the discharge, and a rate-of-flow indicator. This bench may be of single-meter capacity or designed for simultaneous testing of a number of meters (Figure 5-4).

Similar equipment should be provided for testing meters larger than 1 in. An additional tank, 100 ft^3 or 1,000 gal (5 m^3) or larger, should be provided for testing 3-in. (80-mm) and larger meters. Commercial testing is available for all meter sizes used in modern utilities, including fire-line meters (see Figures 5-5 and 5-6). A rate-of-flow indicator of larger capacity is also essential.

Procedure

Although the following description covers the actual steps in testing a single $\frac{5}{8}$-in. (15-mm) meter, the only differences for larger meters are the rates of flow and test quantities used. Test equipment is the same as that previously described.

1. Clamp the meter securely to the test bench. (Do not tighten more than necessary to make a watertight connection, as there is a possibility of distorting the meter housing or extruding the washer into the waterway.)

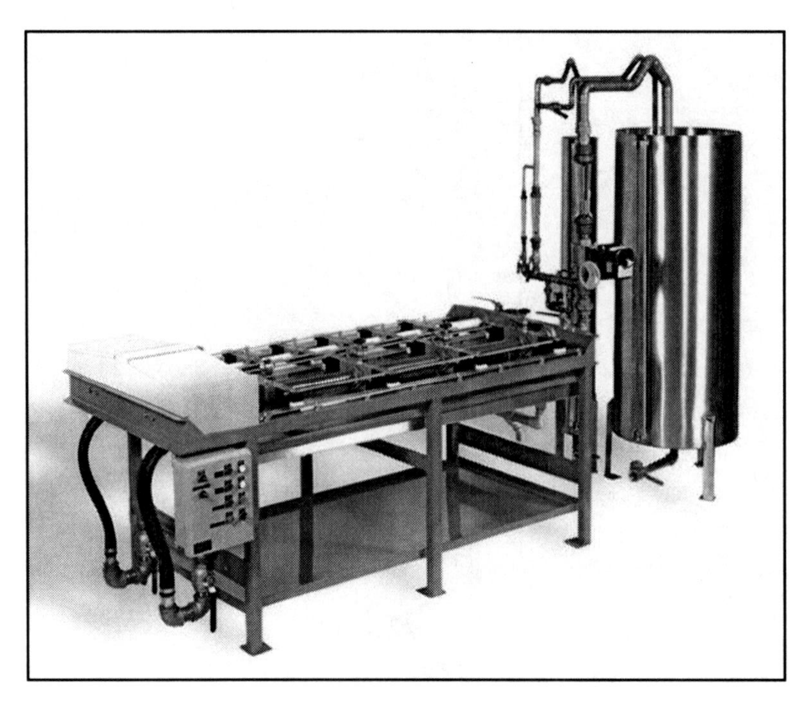

This test bench can test ⅝-in. (15-mm), ⅝-in. × ¾-in. (15-mm × 20-mm), or 1-in. (25-mm) meters. The unit features a rate-of-flow indicator and an electronically actuated shutoff valve, with two calibrated tanks. This style bench features mechanically operated clamping mechanisms.

Courtesy: MARS Company

Figure 5-4 Test bench for small meters

This test bench can test 3-in. (80-mm) through 12-in. (300-mm) water meters of different types. Multiple meters can be tested depending on their size and length. A hydraulic system is used to clamp the meters in place, and the bench is operated using a programmable gravimetric system. All water is recirculated.

Courtesy: Dallas Water Utilities

Figure 5-5 Testing of large meters

This test facility includes two 50-hp pumps rated at 1,250 gpm (284 m^3/h) each. It includes two 5,000-gal or 500-ft^3 (19-m^3) tanks in addition to several smaller tanks, all based on gravimetric systems.

Courtesy: Las Vegas Valley Water District

Figure 5-6 Large meter testing facility

2. Open the register cover.
3. Open the discharge valve first, then open the inlet valve gradually and run the water to waste until the entrapped air is cleared. This process also ensures a full discharge line to the tank.
4. Shut off the discharge valve.
5. Check 100-gal or 10-ft^3 (0.5-m^3) tank discharge to ensure that the tank is empty and then close the tank drain valve. (Tank discharge should be to an open drain so that any possible leakage of the tank drain valve can also be observed.)
6. Record the correct meter reading carefully. The purge cycle procedure takes up any possible backlash in the gearing.
7. Open the test bench discharge valve as rapidly as prudently possible to the desired rate for the maximum-flow test (15 gpm [3.4 m^3/h]). Continue the flow at this rate until the meter reaches the desired quantity. Read the meter accuracy from the scale of the calibrated tank (Figure 5-7) or, if the tank is not calibrated, by weighing the water in the tank. Trickling or bumping water through the meter to accomplish an exact volume of measurement is not recommended. If the indicated test volume shown by the meter under test is not exactly equal to the nominal test quantity that had been intended, the meter accuracy calculation must include consideration of the actual volume indicated by the test meter (see similar considerations under the section on "Multiple-Meter Testing" that follows).

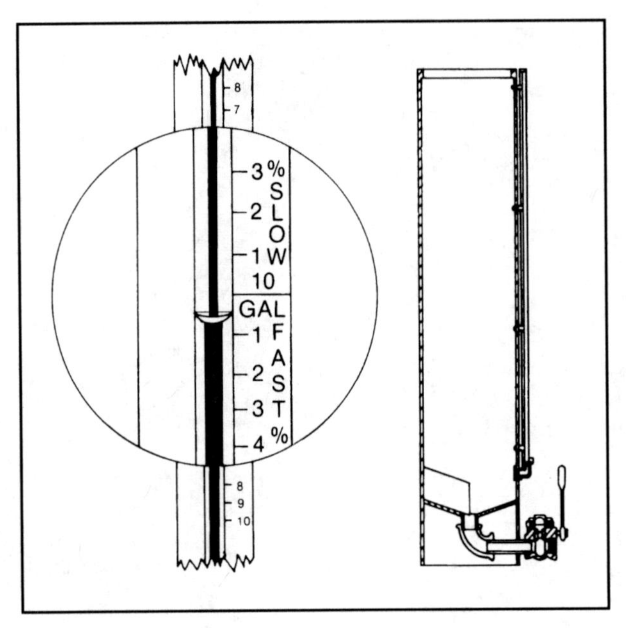

The calibration scale shows the amount by which the tested meter is over- or underregistering, in percent. The reading illustrated is 0.5 percent fast (meter registers 100.5 percent of true quantity passed through it).

Figure 5-7 Detail of calibration scale of testing tank and sectional view of tank with outlet valve

8. Record the results of this test on the record form or log data into the computers used for meter management.

9. If the meter being tested is a repaired meter and its accuracy does not fall within prescribed limits, use calibration adjustments or new parts to bring the unit within limits. Repeat the test as outlined. Be sure that the meter tests correctly by rerunning the test after any changes are made.

10. If a repaired meter is being tested and is found to register within the limits on the maximum-flow test rate, repeat steps 3 through 8 for the intermediate (2 gpm [0.5 m^3/h]) and minimum (¼ gpm [0.06 m^3/h]) tests, discharging the test water into the 10-gal or 1-ft^3 [0.05-m^3] tank. The test quantity for these rates is only 10 gal or 1 ft^3 (0.05 m^3), and the meter register test hand completes only one full revolution.

11. If, however, the test is to determine the condition of a meter removed from service, it is recommended to rearrange the order of test flows. The preferable order in this event is the minimum-, intermediate-, and, finally, the maximum-flow test. If a meter that has been in service for some length of time is tested first on the high rate of flow, the possibility exists of freeing the disc and thereby obtaining a false impression of the meter's condition on lower rates. Conversely, a meter should be tested as soon as possible after removal from service to prevent the drying of deposits in the measuring chamber, as this condition tends to give an adverse impression of the meter's condition while it was in service.

12. After the three separate tests have been run, the meter has been fully tested and may be removed from the test bench after the inlet valve of the test bench has been closed and pressure has been released by a partial opening of the discharge valve.

13. Once the test is concluded, the meter should be drained, the register sealed, and the dust caps placed on the meter spuds before the meters are put in storage.

The calibration of a tank is based on its rated capacity, and if lesser quantities are used in testing, as is sometimes done, the calibrated percentage errors are not valid.

It should be noted that a rate-of-flow indicator is affected by water temperature below the 1-gpm (0.2-m^3/h) rate. Most rate-of-flow indicators are calibrated for 69°F (21°C), and density changes due to temperature affect the reading.

Rate-of-flow indicators are usually equipped with a pointer to indicate true rates at the minimum-flow points. They are raised for low-temperature water and lowered for high-temperature water due to changes in water density. A calibrated cylinder and a stopwatch are effective calibrating instruments for the ¼- and ½-gal points; or the following formula may be used to verify the actual rate of flow during a standard accuracy test:

$$RT = V$$

Where:

R = rate of flow, gpm

T = time of flow, min

V = volume of test tank, gal

Example: It takes 4 min to fill a 1-gal calibrated cylinder at ¼ gpm:

$$R = \frac{V}{T} = \frac{1}{4} = \frac{1}{4} \text{ gpm}$$

This check on the accuracy of low-flow calibration should be considered when a marked change in water temperature of the test water occurs, or the entire test volume should be timed for the actual flow rate.

Multiple-Meter Testing

Multiple testing of meters is identical to the testing of one meter, except for one important factor. In multiple-meter testing, it is not possible to use the meter test dials for determining the test quantity, as each meter has a slightly different accuracy. The test quantity is discharged into the tank of known volume, and the flow is stopped when the scale on the tank indicates that the exact quantity has been delivered. Using gravimetrics, the flow is stopped when the electronic scale indicates that the exact quantity has been achieved. Each meter's accuracy is determined by reading its register. The arithmetic of the test must be clearly understood when meters are tested volumetrically. Gravimetric systems that are automated compute the accuracy for each meter as the correct reading is entered by the technician. In the tests described for testing one ⅝-in. (15-mm) meter, only two quantities were used, 100 gal or 10 ft^3 (0.5 m^3) for the maximum-flow test and 10 gal or 1 ft^3 (0.05 m^3) for the intermediate- and minimum-flow tests. One full revolution of the test hand of a ⅝-in. (15-mm) meter registers either 10 gal or 1 ft^3, and the test-hand circle is divided into 10 equal parts. Therefore, on the maximum-flow test, when the test hand makes 10 full revolutions, each 1 gal subdivision of the test dial circle is a 1 percent variation. On the intermediate- and minimum-flow tests of 10 gal or 1 ft^3, the test hand makes only one revolution, and each subdivision represents a 10 percent variation.

When ⅝-in. (15-mm) meters are tested in groups and the exact test quantity is discharged into the tank, the percentage of error between divisions of the test dial depends on the quantity, i.e., 1 percent for 100 gal or 10 ft^3 and 10 percent for 10 gal or 1 ft^3. Furthermore, it must be determined whether the meter is fast or slow. If, in group testing ⅝-in. (15-mm) meters on a quantity of 100 gal, the test hand of one meter has made 10 full revolutions plus one additional mark (1 gal), the meter has registered 101 gal when only 100 gal were delivered; and the meter is registering 101 percent of true quantity, or 1 percent fast. Similarly, if the test hand of another meter has made 10 revolutions minus two marks (2 gal), it registers only 98 gal when 100 gal are being delivered and, therefore, is registering 98 percent of true quantity, or 2 percent slow.

When 10 gal or 1 ft^3 are used in multiple testing, each division of the test dial circle represents 10 percent error, and if a meter register shows on the test that the test hand has only moved 9/10 of the full circle, it is registering only 90 percent. It is always necessary to interpolate between the marks for more accurate readings.

Although concern is often expressed over the time involved in testing meters on low rates of flow and large test quantities, multiple testing of meters reduces this factor on a unit basis. Furthermore, a relatively low-cost, automatic, electric cutoff valve can be installed in the test bench unit, which eliminates the need for someone to stand by to ensure against overrun of the test. This attachment, shown in Figure 5-8, consists of an electric valve with a strainer, a relay with transformer, one low-voltage electrode for each tank, and the necessary wiring and switches. When the water in the tank rises to the test volume level, this causes the relay contacts to open, and causes the valve to close and stop the flow. Gravimetric systems are usually supplied with automatic shut-off for greater accuracy. (See Figure 5-9 for a large multiple-testing operation.)

When multiple-meter tests are made on multijet meters, two suitable conditions should be provided: (1) a constant, nonpulsating flow; and (2) intermediate coupling pieces between the meters having the same bore diameter as that of the meter and having a length between three and five times that of the diameter.

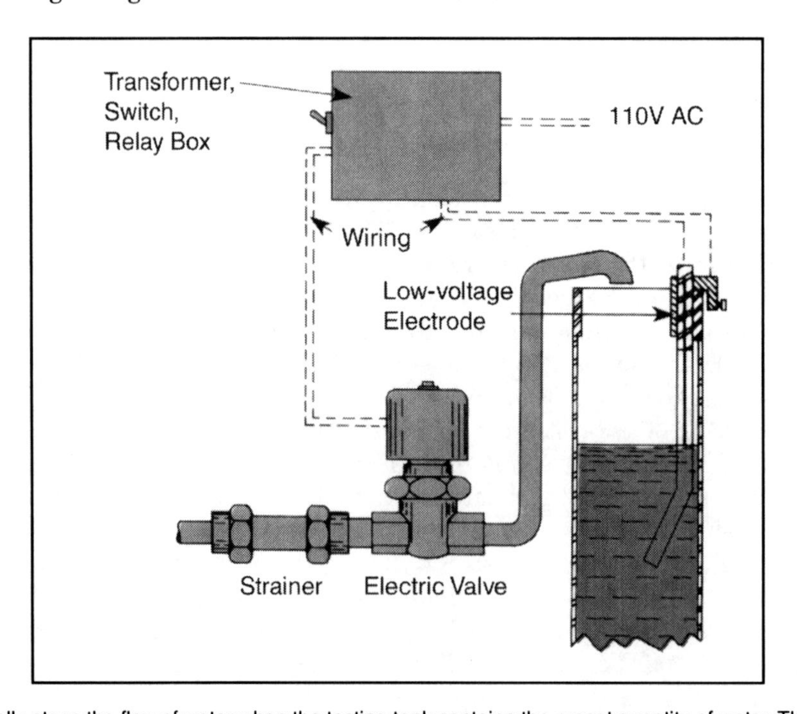

This device automatically stops the flow of water when the testing tank contains the preset quantity of water. This feature eliminates the need for someone to stand watch to ensure against overrun of the test.

Figure 5-8 Automatic cutoff valve

This bench can test ⅝ in. and ¾ in. meters in production quantities. Two rows at a time are tested at high, medium, and low flow rates.

Courtesy: MARS Company

Figure 5-9 Large multiple-meter test bench

FIELD TESTING

Larger meters are frequently ignored as long as they continue to record consumption. These meters may be few in number, but they represent a significant amount of revenue for a water system. Typically, the largest 10 percent of the meters measure 40 to 60 percent of a system's consumption.

Considering the fact that larger meters are so important to a water system's financial health, why are they not maintained to provide peak performance? The answer is that older meters are harder to work on and repair; spare parts are expensive; assemblies are sometimes complex; and it takes more knowledge and better-trained repair personnel to maintain them than for smaller meters. Modern large meters, like turbines, compounds, and fire-line meters, are currently being produced in modular designs with consideration for regular maintenance.

These larger meters are so important that their operating condition must be monitored on a systematic and timely basis. One alternative approach is for qualified test personnel to test these meters on-site.

On-Site Testing Rationale

On-site testing of larger meters is one way to ensure their proper operation; another is to test the production meters at the water system's facilities. There are certain advantages to testing the meters at the water system's facilities. In the majority of situations, on-site testing is more economical in time and resources. From a technical standpoint, the piping in a meter installation can have a definite influence on a meter's accuracy, and this irregularity can be detected by the on-site tests.

The diagram in Figure 4-6 specifies correct meter installations. Properly operating isolation valves and a straight pipe, a minimum of 5 pipe diameters in front of the meter and a minimum of 3 pipe diameters downstream of the test tee, are critical in attaining engineered accuracy and performance.

One acceptable method of maintaining proper performance of certain types of larger meters is to replace the operating components and assemblies while leaving the meter body in place. If the measuring and registration functions are within one integral assembly and shop tested, accuracy tests are not required after installation. If separate assemblies are involved, a final on-site accuracy test is appropriate. Without accuracy testing of separate assemblies, the potential loss of significant revenue increases.

Because of the revenue these large meters produce, a formal on-site meter testing program should be part of every water system's maintenance operation. Increased revenue and water accountability gains will offset the initial investment and continuing costs of the testing programs. Actual case histories at Boston, Mass., East Orange, N.J., Columbia, S.C., and other utilities have shown such returns to be both immediate and dramatic.*

What's Involved With On-Site Testing

Setting up and maintaining an on-site meter testing program involves a number of factors. The meter pit must have adequate and safe space in which personnel can maneuver. Occupational Safety and Health Administration (OSHA) requirements must be adhered to, and everyone in the testing program should be clearly instructed on its guidelines. The piping arrangement around the meter must include some method to positively isolate the meter, while still maintaining an adequate flow to the end user. Temporary or permanent by-pass piping needs to be installed.

Some larger meters have built-in test plugs; others do not. Test ports may not be suitable for some higher flow rates. For installations that require test outlets, the outlets can be fabricated in a number of ways. Service saddles and reducing tees are the most frequently used approaches. These need to be installed according to the recommendations of the meter manufacturer and located so that the connecting hose to the on-site tester is correctly located downstream of the meter.

A prerequisite to testing is that the isolating, downstream shutoff valve provides positive shutoff. If the valve is not completely operational and leakage occurs when the valve is in the off position, the test will not be accurate.

To assist the testing operation, a short length of pipe should be permanently attached to the test outlet, along with a shutoff valve that can be locked into position. This will save considerable time and effort in preparing the meter site for testing.

Finally, and most importantly, the personnel assigned to perform the tests must be properly trained and have the appropriate test equipment. Certain techniques and procedures must be properly followed when using the test equipment. The consequences of discharging large volumes of water at high flow rates must be understood, appreciated, and accounted for. Some utilities actually capture test water for conservation and use elsewhere. Improper use of the equipment can be harmful to the operators, the meter, and the surrounding area.

The techniques for performing the tests, selecting the appropriate test flow rates, determining the accuracies, and reaching conclusions, must be known and carefully followed to obtain valid test results. Meter testers should be considered specialists.

---

* Data is available from Schlumberger Industries.

Types of Test Equipment

Residential meters, meters up to 1 in. (25 mm) in size, can be tested on-site in several ways to determine accuracy. The test equipment (Figure 5-10) and methods for determining the accuracy of these meters are not applicable to testing the larger meters. The larger meters require specialized test equipment that can handle a wide range of flow rates and provide accurate, valid data. These devices can either be purchased as a manufactured assembly or fabricated by the water utility.

The equipment for the larger meters (Figure 5-11) is available as portable test packages, installed on trailers, or mounted in a van (Figures 5-12 and 5-13) or pickup truck.

Regardless of the style, these testers all contain certain basic elements that are required to properly test turbine, compound, and propeller meters.

Because of the wide flow ranges involved, a tester includes at least two, and sometimes three, meters of varying capacities. A shutoff valve is located downstream of each meter to control the flow rate for the various tests. A pressure gauge is required to check both the line pressure and the residual pressure at the tester. Sometimes resettable registers and/or flow raters are included to reduce the time required to complete a test.

Flexible hoses are required to connect the test equipment to the test connection of the meter being tested. Because of the pressures and hydraulic forces, the hoses must be in good condition and positioned as straight as possible between the two meters. For the larger testers, it is important that the tester itself be anchored to a vehicle, or a hold-down device, because the tester will want to move when the flow is shut off.

The master meters used on the testers must be capped, protected, and handled with care when not in use. They should also be recalibrated periodically using standards that are traceable to a national standard such as the National Institute of Standards and Technology (NIST) or Measurement Canada.

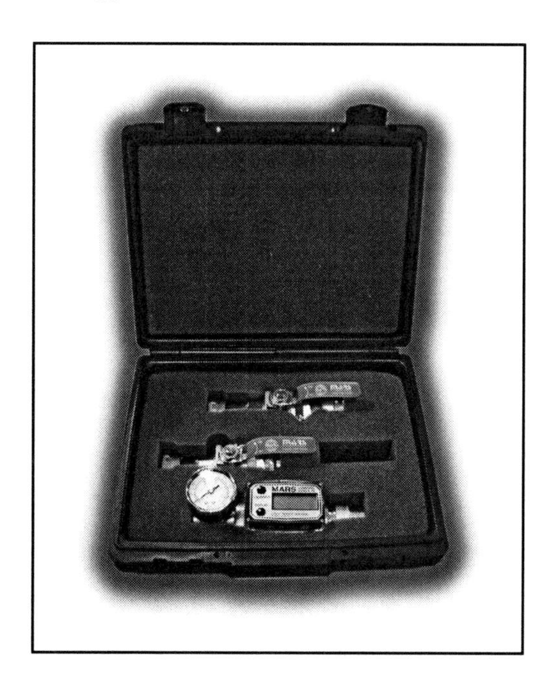

Courtesy: MARS Company

Figure 5-10 Field-test apparatus for small meters

Courtesy: MARS Company

Courtesy: Sensus Technologies Inc.

Figure 5-11 Field testing flanged meters

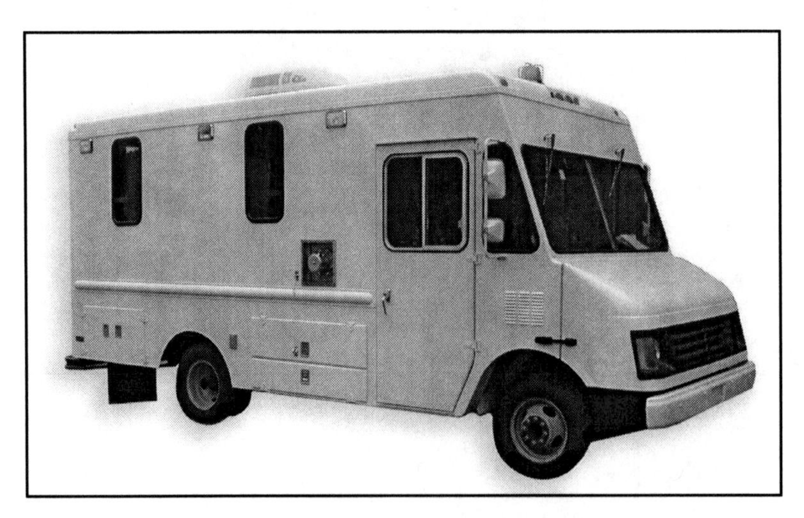

The mobile meter test van is capable of testing meter sizes 3 in. (80 mm) to 12 in. (300 mm) without removing the meters from service. The unit is self-contained, computer driven, and fully automatic.

Courtesy: MARS Company

Figure 5-12 Mobile meter test van

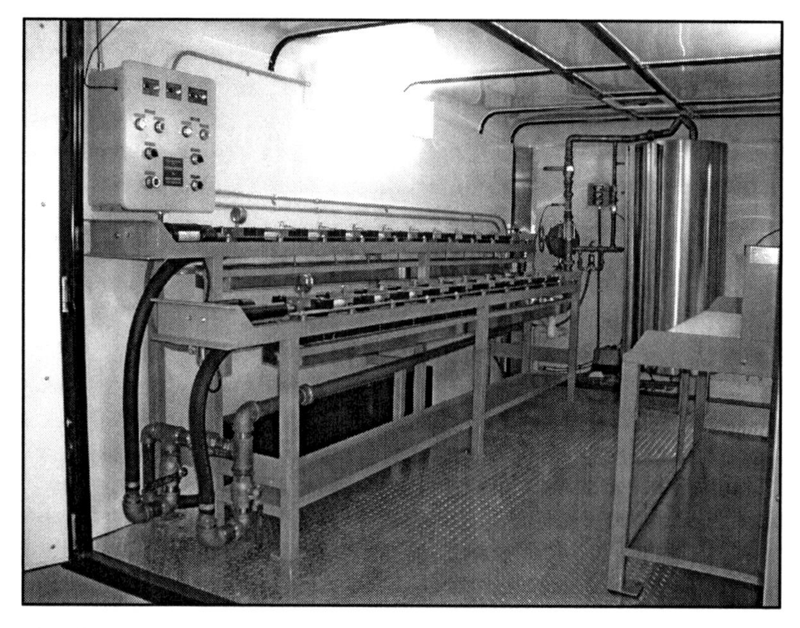

A portable testing system installed in a trailer.

Courtesy: MARS Company

Figure 5-13 Mobile test unit

Test Procedure

Before testing, it is necessary to know what the typical accuracy curve of the meter is for each specific brand, model, and size of meter being tested. This information can be obtained from the meter manufacturer's literature. A chart can be prepared that lists the flow rates at which each meter should be tested to properly assess its operational condition. Table 5-3 will suffice in the absence of factory data.

For positive displacement meters, chapter 2 of this manual provides the three flow rates (low, mid, and high) which apply to all meter brands. For turbine and propeller meters, either this manual or the meter literature should be consulted. For compound meters, it is important to know where "cross-over" is located so that it can be specifically tested. For this information, the manufacturer's accuracy curves are preferable. (Different brands of compounds have various cross-over flow rates. A discussion of these cross-over flow rates is beyond the scope of this manual.)

The various suppliers of large-meter test equipment provide detailed procedures for conducting the accuracy tests. In general, the tester is hooked up and the line flushed. The flow rate should be set to flush the testing apparatus, and the leak test should be conducted by observing the meter flow indicator.

Considerations When Testing

When testing a meter on-site, compare the accuracy of the meter in question to another, calibrated meter. The calibrated meter has its own performance characteristics and is not 100 percent accurate across its entire flow range, unless it is electronically corrected to level the accuracy curve. Other than at the very low flows, where the acceptable accuracy is 95 percent (minimum), differences of 1 or 2 percent should not be a concern.

Once the testing begins, the testing order is from the low flows to the higher flows. Experience has shown that when most meters begin to wear or lose accuracy, it occurs at the lower flows rather than the higher. If a meter is performing accurately up through the lower 25 percent of its capacity, it will typically test accurately through the rest of the range. This is especially true on the very large meters.

Another item to consider is what to do with the water after it has gone through the tester. A sudden high flow rate, such as one thousand gallons per minute, could reduce the supply pressure available and disturb any debris in the service line to the customer. It could also reduce the water supply in a nearby portion of the system, or it could cause considerable damage if the water is not discharged properly. Sheet ice on the street is a major life-threatening hazard. Great care should be taken to prevent water from freezing on the road surface or walking surfaces near the test site.

When setting up the tests, no test should be less than one minute long, and the meter's sweep hand should make at least one complete revolution. The residual pressure on the tester should never be less than 20 psi (140 kPa) when running a high-flow test. Also, for safety, the tester should not be operated on lines with static pressure exceeding 80 psi (550 kPa) unless provisions are made to secure the tester.

Detailed records are important to monitor trends in performance, along with the accuracies obtained at the various flow rates. Record the meter's registration before and after the testing, so the customer is not charged for the water used during the test. Portable computers and test software makes this job easy and accurate.

The local utility must determine how inaccurate a meter can become before repairs or replacement can be justified. A cost-versus-benefit consideration is required, based on a number of factors important to the local water system. The considerations should also include the sizing and the selection of the replacement meter. Another factor should be the updating of the meter installation for future on-site testing.

This page intentionally blank.

Chapter 6

Maintenance and Repair of Water Meters

INTRODUCTION

Millions of water meters are in service in the United States. While these meters represent a sizable investment for water utilities, their real value cannot be realized unless they are functioning efficiently. Many of the meters presently in service are more than 20 years old.

In the past, the design of these meters was complex and cumbersome, and their performance, even when new, was not comparable to modern meter designs. Modern technology is providing meters with tighter accuracy specifications, lower head loss, and greatly simplified maintenance.

Most modern meters except electronic solid-state meters contain magnetic couplings and sealed registers. This design concept eliminates the highly maintenance-prone stuffing box; heavy, wet-running gear train; and exposed register. Additionally, most modern meters contain synthetic polymer components that are resistant to corrosion.

The success of the synthetic polymer chamber and magnetic coupled sealed registers have reduced maintenance costs dramatically. Meter shops are still the best opportunity to maintain meter accuracy and protect the related revenue (Figure 6-1). The skills needed to maintain water meters have changed. Older complex meters with gear trains required skilled craftsmen, whereas the modern sealed register meters are made of components that can be quickly exchanged by a technician with limited training. Utilities usually dispose of the outmoded meters by selling them as scrap or through a trade-in allowance against new meter purchases. Although a period of regular replacement of meters instead of repairs was used for a time, modern meters are more advanced, more accurate, and too costly to simply scrap on a regular basis. In addition, the need to test meters has not gone away, given customer issues and the need to ensure revenue protection.

Courtesy: Elster AMCO Water Inc.

Figure 6-1 A meter technician maintaining modern concept water meters (left: endurance test; right: accuracy test)

Many meters experience light usage over normal periods and may provide additional service. It may be more prudent to measure the life of a meter by total consumption rather than by time. It is rarely advisable to repair outdated or obsolete designs, but modern meters are modular in design, making them easier to repair. Encoder-type, high-tech meters, including radio-equipped units, are simply too expensive to throw away without a proper evaluation and test to determine serviceability. An evaluation of cost per meter repaired is valuable in making this decision.

METER REPLACEMENT

A planned meter replacement program can be implemented over a given number of years; for example, 10 percent of the meters each year over 10 years, or 20 percent per year over 5 years, so that all replaced meters in the system will be the more efficient, modern design. Concurrently, all additional meters purchased for expansion will be of the modern design, and the entire system will be upgraded on a planned schedule. This provides the utility with two advantages:

1. The meters in service are far more efficient in their ability to measure all water consumed and to recover maximum revenue for the utility.
2. The expenses of maintaining, stocking, staffing, and operating a traditional repair shop are greatly reduced by a regular meter maintenance program.

Modern magnetic-drive meters and electronic meters contain very few service parts; therefore, the ongoing maintenance becomes one of simply replacing the major components rather than laboriously hand reworking, cleaning, and reassembling a multitude of miscellaneous parts. All major meter manufacturers offer factory-built, measuring-assembly replacements that can be installed by low-skilled workers. Most also offer replacement register assemblies. The materials used in the measuring chambers and registers have eliminated cleaning or replacement due to corrosion.

The traditional meter shop has, and will continue, to change to match the modern technology used to create today's water meter. There will always be a requirement for maintenance and upgrading of existing meters. It will be done on a very simplified replacement-by-assembly basis in the near term and possibly by adopting the replacement-meter concept in the long term, if inflation and increased labor costs so dictate.

METER MAINTENANCE AND REPAIR

Detailing of specific procedures is impossible in a text of this scope because of the variations in design of the different brands. On request, established manufacturers will provide specialized information if required on repairing meters of their own make. They should be consulted in advance for procedures especially applicable to their meters.

Dismantling and Cleaning

In the past, meters were cleaned by sandblasting or bead-blasting and by acid baths. These proved to be environmentally unfriendly and even dangerous.

Modern meter shops still use some bead-blasting equipment but only with approved dust recovery systems. Mild biodegradable soap baths are adequate for cleaning internal parts. Painting has also been eliminated for environmental reasons and the fact that bronze and polymer meters simply do not need to be externally painted to be accurate and serviceable.

It is recommended shop practice to clean the exterior of the meters first to avoid introduction of dirt into the meter repair shop. Sand- or bead-blasting is an efficient cleaning method. Wire brushing and hand scrubbing can also be used. Sandblasting may be used only on outer casings.

DISASSEMBLING

After the exterior cleaning is completed, the meter should be dismantled into its basic components of the shell or case, usually an upper and a lower part, the register, and the measuring chamber.

Power tools with torque-limiting capability are useful for speeding up assembly and disassembly of meters. The use of pneumatic, rather than electric, tools is recommended for safety.

Casings. Bronze casings should be checked for distortion caused by frost. If damaged, the casing must be replaced. The meter should then be cleaned of all gasketing material with a suitable tool.

The threads on the inlet and outlet spuds should then be checked. If they are nicked or otherwise damaged, they can be repaired by running a rethreading die over them. Note that the threads on all meters having external threads are straight threads, rather than tapered, and the thread dimensions must be as required in ANSI/AWWA C700, which conform to ASME B1.20.1.

Register boxes. Modern meter registers that are damaged should be replaced with a new sealed register assembly. If the lid or serial number plate is bent or broken at the hinge, it should be replaced.

Modern water meters have fully sealed gears and cannot be serviced. Older gear-trained-equipped meters are not upgradable to modern sealed registers or automatic meter-reading equipment. These units are obsolete and should be replaced. The scrap brass should be sold to recover part of the original investment.

Measuring chambers. The measuring chamber is the heart of the meter, and it is this chamber that determines the meter's characteristics and accuracy (Figures 6-2 and 6-3). Measuring chambers are of several types, commonly referred to as the nutating-disc type, oscillating-piston, multijet, turbine, fluidic oscillator, singlejet, and others used in large meters.

Several meter manufacturers have available chamber-exchange programs with guaranteed accuracy for moderate costs.

A special prying tool (left) is used to open a two-part chamber. A metal ball gauge (right) may be used to check the socket in the measuring chamber for wear. This is an early predecessor to the modern polymer disc chamber.

Figure 6-2 Opening of disc chamber and gauging of chamber ball socket

Correct fit and clearance in the disc and chamber largely determine the accuracy of the meter.

Figure 6-3 Examination and assembly of chamber and disc

Reassembly and Testing

Reassembly involves the assembly of components, including the main case, measuring chamber, and register assembly. Bottom plates can be polymer, cast iron, or bronze. Frost-proof bottom plates are designed to break and protect the higher value meter main case. The measuring chamber may incur some damage and require replacement.

MECHANICAL-DRIVE METER REASSEMBLY

Some utilities still use some mechanical drive meters, but these are obsolete and are being replaced as new designs are introduced.

Every repaired meter should be tested for accuracy. Recommended accuracy standards for various rates of flow in repaired meters are given in chapter 5.

REPAIR OF MAGNETIC-DRIVE METERS

Registers. There are two types of registers used on magnetic-drive meters. One is a permanently sealed unit that is not repairable. If damaged, this entire unit must be returned to the manufacturer and repaired or replaced. The majority of modern meters are produced with permanently sealed registers.

In the repairable register, the register housing is fastened to the main casing with screws and sealed with an O-ring.

CONCLUSION

Due to modern meter engineering design, material costs, and manufacturers' programs, many meter repair shops have limited their scope of repairs. Meter testing for revenue protection and minor repairs are the new state of the art. Each water utility must study the economics of meter repair versus meter replacement. Modern meters are produced with very few serviceable modular parts; therefore, replacement programs are more feasible than repair programs. Although cost-effective repairs may be limited in scope, the maintenance through testing of water meters should continue, to ensure equity among customers and minimal revenue loss resulting from underregistration of meters. Modern meters with automatic meter reading (AMR) systems are replacing many older obsolete designs. These meters are much more accurate and can produce more revenue due to their accuracy and ease of service. Even utilities that are not yet using modern AMR systems should consider meters that are easily convertible to these systems in the future.

This page intentionally blank.

Chapter 7

Maintenance Shop Layout and Equipment

INTRODUCTION

The gradual realization of the true value of potable water has made water metering an important activity for many water utilities. Meter companies have worked to constantly improve meter accuracy to ensure water utilities receive all the revenue they deserve. The actual cost to produce water that meets today's quality standards has increased dramatically; therefore, much more is at risk if meter accuracy is not maintained at the highest possible level. Meter accuracy has also become more important as the practice of using the water meter reading to invoice for wastewater operations has become more widespread. Many unmetered "flat rate" communities are metering for one or more reasons, including the following: (1) to conserve water in a water-deficient area to ensure that an adequate water supply is available for the future; (2) to equitably distribute water production and delivery costs over the range of users; and (3) to collect financial resources for growth and maintenance.

As additional communities become metered, they will need to establish and operate meter testing and maintenance programs or repair shops using the knowledge and the experience of the water works industry. While meter repair services are available in some areas, sound economics dictate that a utility establish and operate its own meter test and repair facility once the number of repairs is large enough to justify a professional testing program.

Water has become more widely recognized as an important natural resource and, as a result, water utilities have had opportunities to develop effective meter repair and replacement programs. It is important to develop an efficient meter repair shop through proper equipment selection and meter shop layout. Many meter shops are housed in existing facilities, and space constraints place operational restrictions on management. When the opportunity arrives to modernize through remodeling or rebuilding, management should be prepared to optimize meter departments with the proper equipment and an efficient layout. Architect consultants can provide valuable assistance, but they must be advised on the necessary features and functions of a meter shop to provide for an adequate supply of test water. In cases with substantial test volume throughput or with water effluent concerns, use of recirculation systems should also be considered. USE regulates discharges into streams and waterways (i.e., waters of the United States) through its National Pollutant Discharge Elimination System (NPDES), and meter testing programs should ensure compliance with these regulations.

Meter shops come in all sizes and shapes with the capability of handling from a few dozen to many thousands of meters each year. Adequate space is essential to provide for an efficient operation. Conditions that can affect the size, equipment, and layout of a meter repair shop include the following:

- Total number of water meters in the system and the projection for future growth.
- Ability to test, repair, or replace modern electronics like AMR systems.
- Variety of makes, sizes, and types of water meters to be serviced.
- Extent of repair capabilities desired and/or required.
- Knowledge to recommend repairing, modernizing, or salvaging aging meter models.
- Water quality in the system. This can have an effect on meter corrosion, lining dezincification, and wear.
- Local practice or the state requirements specifying how often meters must be tested and local code requirements for properly approved installations.
- Private ownership of meters, which may call for the identification and the segregation of meters to ensure that they can be returned to the proper owners.
- Requirements for private owners to test or repair aging meters using authorized or certified installers.
- Requirements that all privately owned meters can be tested at any time by the water utility to ensure correct revenue maintenance.
- Special cleaning/painting requirements to satisfy USE requirements and company policy.
- Ventilation system to exhaust fumes from meter shops and enclosed spaces.
- General plant services available, including:
    - Air at appropriate pressure and volume sufficient to handle all equipment
    - Water at appropriate pressure and volume at maximum flow
    - Available electric energy and lighting
    - Water drains and/or recycling capabilities
- Meter inventory handling and control procedures.

METER SHOP EQUIPMENT

Because reliable equipment is essential for producing quality work, basic shop equipment should include testing equipment, cleaning equipment, and work stations.

Testing Equipment

The following sections provide a discussion of a variety of equipment used in testing water-meter performance.

Test bench for meter sizes ⅝ in. (15 mm) through 2 in. (50 mm). The size of the test bench and the number of meters that can be tested at one time is determined by the work load. A large meter shop may need one or more test benches for the most common size residential meter and larger commercial/industrial meters. Factory-built test equipment for residential size meters is readily available.

Each test bench should be equipped with appropriate valves, pressure gauges, and a rate-of-flow measuring device. Hydraulic clamping to secure meters in the test bench and automatic water shutoff at preset testing levels will increase efficiency.

Test uncertainties can be reduced through the use of gravimetric tanks. Weighting system scales should comply with applicable national standards.

Test station for meter sizes 3 in. (80 mm) and larger. Equipment for testing 3 in. (80 mm) and larger meters varies greatly based on the quantity of various size and type of water meters. Many test benches can safely test meters up to 30 in. in diameter. Test stands can be designed and fabricated locally but should always include provisions for convenient exchange of meters with different dimensions. Overhead lifting devices are usually needed in addition to flow measuring devices, pressure gauges, and control valves.

Test tanks. Calibrated tanks of various sizes should be used together with the test bench to contain the water used for testing. In addition, sight tubes on the tanks are necessary to gauge the water level on a volume basis, or gravimetric systems can be used with the tanks for a higher level of accuracy.

Safety Issues

Testing operations can be dangerous and require technician training to ensure maximum safety and production throughput. Water moving at high velocity through a testing device can impart destructive water hammer shocks unless precautions are taken to eliminate these high shocks to a level that will not destroy the meters, the testing equipment, or the water mains in the vicinity of the meter shop.

Most testing operations are relatively safe because the water velocity is controlled by the test bench or the meters have restrictions.

Larger test systems operated by trained technicians are also safe when these simple rules are followed:

1. No test system can be operated at working pressures greater than 150 psi, including any water hammer or pressure surge, unless permitted by a specific standard. ANSI/AWWA C703 should be referenced for the exception. Pressure-reducing devices must be used ahead of the first appliance in the system, including the test equipment and control valves.

2. Quick-closing valves, such as lever-operated ball or butterfly valves, cannot be used without motor operations calculated at a closing rate that will eliminate water hammer.

3. Meters with case damage cannot be tested safely under pressure because of the possible failure of the case causing projectiles, high-pressure water damage, or injury.

4. Emergency shutoffs should be designed to safely shut down all valves and pumps.

5. Automated test systems should be equipped with variable frequency drives (VFDs) to allow pumps to ramp up and down safely to avoid damage to the system or the meter being tested. Pumps should not be set at a pressure greater than 150 psi.

6. Lifting equipment and other special meter-handling devices prevent lifting injuries and other injuries caused by falling meters. It is important to design the shop and the meter-handling equipment to allow technicians to handle and test all meter sizes safely.

7. Field testing has its own special safety issues because of such factors as traffic volume and space confinement. Adequate lifting equipment and service vehicles equipped with safety harnesses and lifting devices should be considered and required.

Meter-Cleaning Equipment

Compressed air with an abrasive or a mild biodegradable soap solution is favorable for cleaning meter parts in preparation for repair and reassembly. Glass beads are the most practical abrasive. Adjusting the air pressure according to the severity of the cleaning problem eliminates possible damage to machined bronze surfaces.

Honing should not be used on plastic or delicate materials. These pieces should be cleaned by other methods described below.

In areas where waters are mild and deposits are soft in nature, hand brushing with warm water and a detergent may be sufficient for cleaning interior meter parts.

Ultrasonic cleaning systems can be used for preparing interior meter parts for repair and reassembly.

All cleaning materials should be disposed of properly. Acid baths or washes or other methods of aggressive chemical cleaning should not be used. These types of cleaning methods are detrimental to the meter materials, violate USE regulations, and may cause significant harm to the user, environment, and water supply.

Painting has been used for more than 50 years in meter shops in North America. Because of the many hazards present in paint fumes, odors, and paint spray damage, most shops have eliminated all painting booths and the related expense. Water meters with a clean bead-blasted outer surface are as reliable as a meter painted with brass-colored paint.

Work Stations

Work stations should be equipped with:

- A workbench with a steel or hardwood working surface for each meter repair station
- A sink with hot and cold running water at each workbench
- Tool compartments that lock
- Compressed air at appropriate pressure and volume at each bench for pneumatic tool use
- Storage bins and drawers for meter parts
- Essential tools
- Any special equipment needed to test AMR devices.

SHOP LAYOUT

Most successful industries have conducted studies in attempts to reduce unnecessary employee movements. These studies have established generally accepted principles applicable to any field of production. Locating equipment to ensure smooth work flow with minimum distances between stations while providing adequate transportation of materials plus temporary storage are the objectives in planning shop layout.

Meter maintenance procedures may vary from shop to shop depending on control procedures (with respect to meters removed) prior to the meters entering the meter shop. In general, however, the procedure for an incoming meter is for the meter to be:

1. Checked for reading and identified as the meter stated on the removal order.
2. Tested for incoming efficiency.

The reasons for meter removal are many, and these reasons usually dictate handling procedures. If the meter is removed for regular replacement due to obsolete technology, inoperative, or not compatible with new AMR systems, management may require an incoming test for revenue analysis purposes or simply place the meter in a scrap holding area for future sale to recycle contractors. If the meter involves a customer complaint or a dispute, special handling and storage is required until the matter is resolved. The decision is then based on the utility's evaluated experience, the meter's registration, its test performance, and normal service life.

When repairs are appropriate, the procedure is as follows, with variations due to local requirements and applicable regulatory standards. The meter to be repaired is:

1. Disassembled and cleaned.
2. Inspected for reassembly with nonserviceable parts being rejected.
3. Fitted with needed new parts and reassembled.
4. Tested for performance and accuracy of registration.
5. Sealed to guard against tampering.

Work flow is the key element to proper shop layout. Depending on the space available, a shop can be designed in a U-shape or in a straight line fashion, with the old meters going in on one side and the rebuilt meters going out of the other. Work stations need to be separated enough so that the mechanics do not interfere with each other, but close enough to avoid unnecessary steps between work areas.

Material handling in a meter test and repair shop is one of the important facets of efficient operation. Depending on the size of the shop, meter processing can be either a continuous or batch operation. Most shops, because of their smaller size, process their meters in batches. The optimum batch is a one test-stand load. Smaller shops that test only small meters below the 2-in. size may have a single mechanic perform each operation required to complete the job. Larger shops that test large meters usually use a two-person team to enhance safety, production speed, and technical expertise.

Transporting meters from processing station to processing station can be conveniently done on carts. In addition to their use as material-handling devices, the carts also serve as in-process storage between stations in the repair cycle.

In general, available space and the bench location dictate shop layout. The best rule of thumb is to design the shop layout to receive meters from the field or from manufacturers through the main receiving area. From there, meters can be diverted through the test and repair section, ending up in a secure storage area awaiting reinstallation. New meters can be inspected and subjected to receiving procedures dictated by company policy and then sent to secure storage. The shop should be laid out with equipment or work stations in the order in which they are used. With the test stand at the end of the process in a U-shaped layout, it is also close to the beginning of the process to facilitate testing of incoming meters. The most frequently used replacement parts should be stored at the work stations.

Good lighting is essential for the worker to be able to do a first-class job.

Each repair bench should have the most frequently used tools on hand, as well as a small sink for special cleanup.

If all water utilities had followed the same processing cycle in repairing meters, standards for equipment and shop layout would have been established in the past. These standards would have varied because of work load, new developments in equipment, and improvements in meter design.

Three shop layouts are shown that satisfy smooth work-flow requirements for the previously detailed meter-repair procedure. U-shaped layouts allow the incoming meters to move smoothly through the shop. Transportation from station to station and temporary storage at any point is provided by a meter cart. Back tracking and cross movements are eliminated. Roller conveyor belts would be practical in a large shop for moving repaired meters from the repair benches to the test bench. In Figures 7-1 to 7-3, the center floor area has been kept open for additional equipment or additional work space, if the work load were to increase or repair procedures were to change. The number of repair benches could be doubled without disturbing the pattern of work flow.

An experienced meter repair supervisor is essential to the operations of a meter maintenance shop. Supervisors must be receptive to suggestions for work simplification from any worker. Obtaining special new equipment and tools, as availability and need are proven, will result in improved quality and increased quantity of work performed. Keeping all parts of any one meter in a metal or fiberglass pan, from disassembly to reassembly, is an example of work simplification. Scheduling repair to one make of meter during any one time period, if the work load permits, simplifies the whole repair procedure. Reviewing test data from the test benches will result in quality control and adherence to established repair standards.

Proper record keeping has been revolutionized by the use of computers, and the modern meter shop needs to be tied into the water department information system. Complete layout planning requires consideration and space for computer data entry, storage, and retrieval.

To summarize, each meter shop will vary in design and layout based on the facilities available and the work to be performed. After those factors are determined and the equipment is selected, a layout can be developed based on time-proven principles of efficient material flow. Considerations to recognize include new health and safety regulations and new environmental laws regarding waste disposal. Plans for new shop layout should be reviewed with management to ensure compliance.

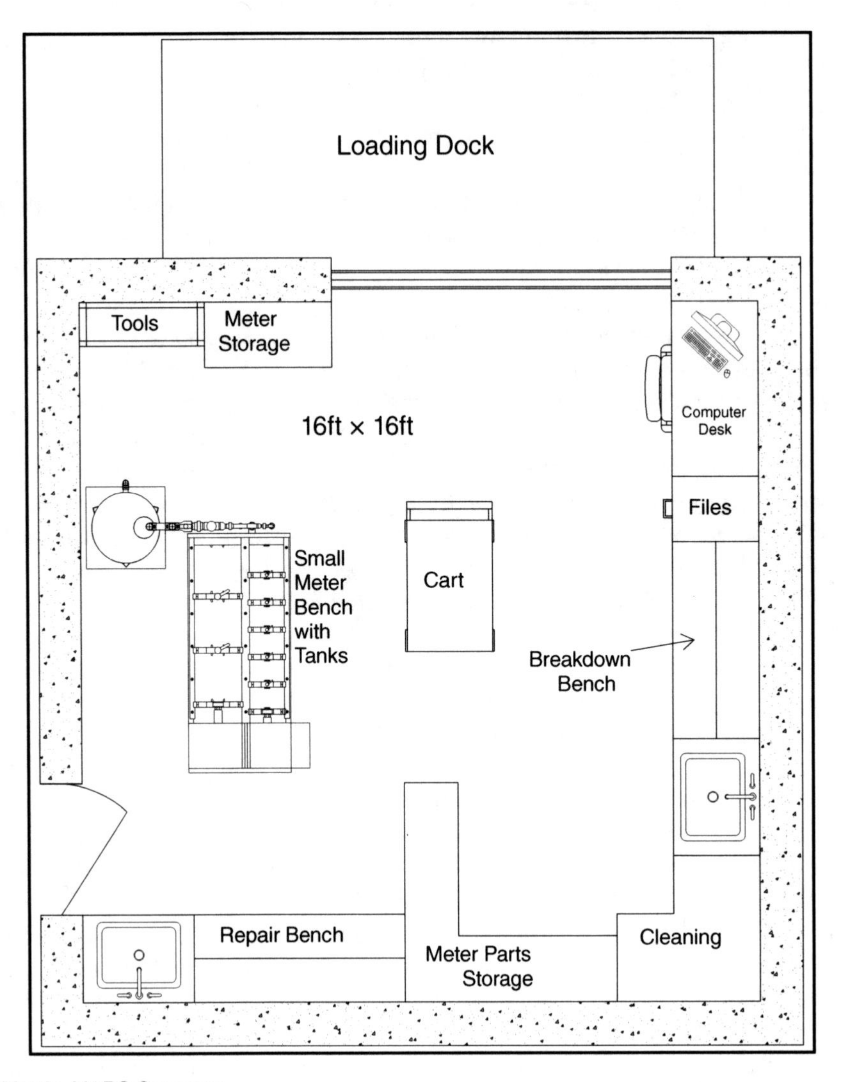

Illustration by Chris Mastic, MARS Company

Figure 7-1 Suggested layout for small modern repair shop

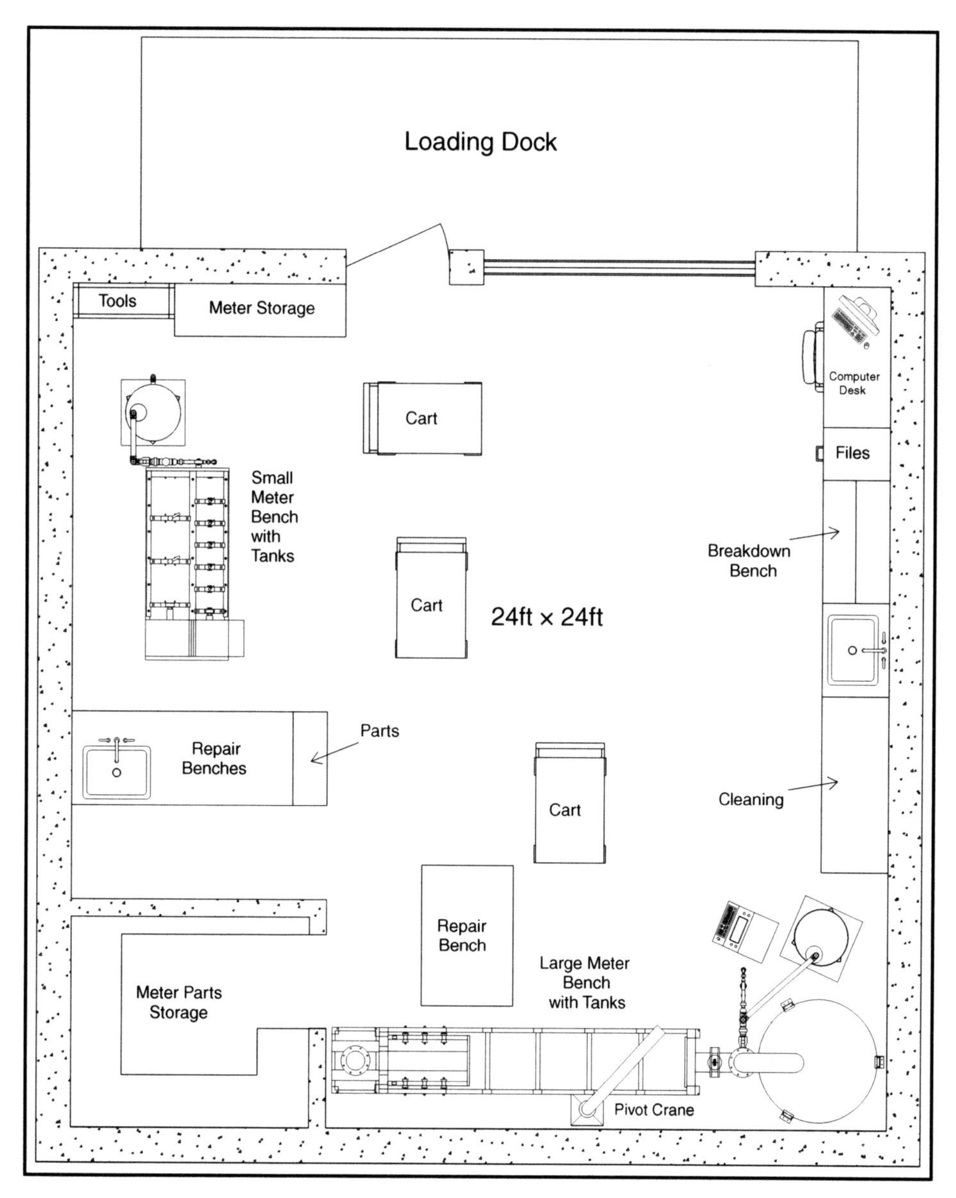

Illustration by Chris Mastic, MARS Company

Figure 7-2 Suggested layout for medium modern repair shop

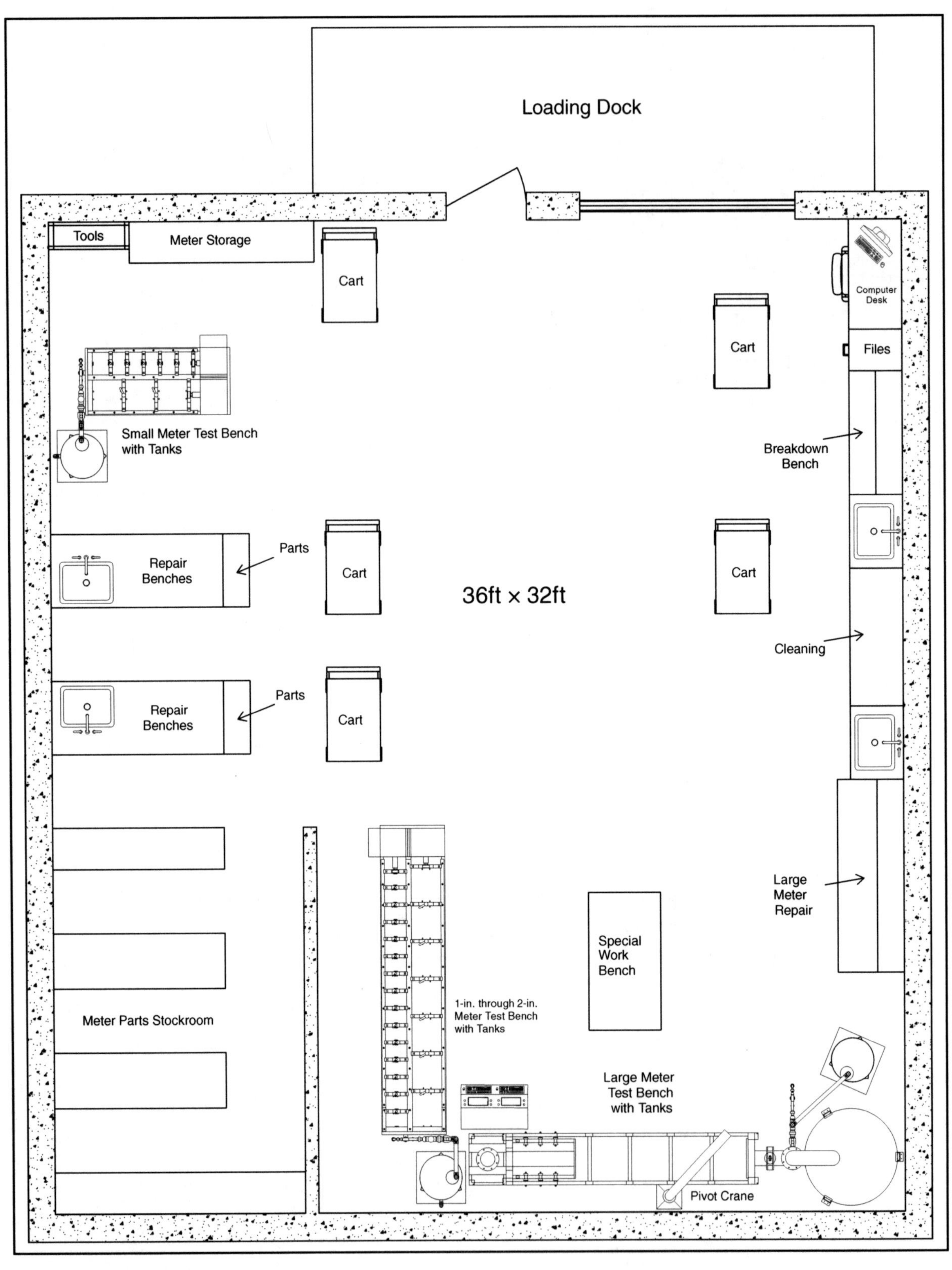

Illustration by Chris Mastic, MARS Company

Figure 7-3 Suggested layout for large modern repair shop

This page intentionally blank.

Chapter 8

Meter Records

INTRODUCTION

A suitable system of meter records provides full and complete information regarding the installation, repair, and testing of each meter with a minimum of expense. In the past, considerable time and effort were needed to maintain meter records. Today, modern computers and meter management software and procedures have improved meter record-keeping practices, including the storage of all test records in a meter records database.

ELEMENTS OF A GOOD RECORD SYSTEM

Meter records should provide basic data for each meter, such as size, make, type, date of purchase, meter location at all times, and testing and repair data. One method of maintaining these records is through the implementation of a fully networked, computer-based tracking system. Because some of the previously mentioned data are often available on a water utility's customer information system (CIS), it is practical to develop a computer-based meter management system to combine customer information with meter records for a usable tool that is part of the main data system. The purchase date, testing, repair information, and previous locations can be entered into this system. In addition, an electronic link can be created between the meter testing shop and the data system for use in generating reports and conducting research.

Each meter purchased should be given its own record in the database, and each record should be given its own unique identifier, usually a number. For example, a utility could use the manufacturer's serial number as each meter's computer record identifier or could identify each meter according to the utility's own meter numbering system if the utility has one.

Meter data should be entered into the system at the time the meter is purchased or first installed in a customer's service or whenever any testing or repair work is done on the meter. These data can be entered directly into the system by the person receiving or repairing/testing the meter. The following listing provides the basic data any record system should contain and includes information that can be found on the system:

- Meter size
- Meter make
- Meter model
- Meter type
- Meter serial number
- Date of purchase
- Current location
- Previous locations
    - Reason for relocation
- Repair history
    - Repair data
    - Type of repair(s)
    - Materials/parts used
    - Labor time
    - Repaired by
    - Comments
- Testing history
    - Testing date(s)
    - Results
        - Minimum rate
        - Intermediate rate
        - Maximum rate
    - Tested by
    - Comments

Each utility must determine how much data are kept on each system.

Sources of Data

Some utilities have replaced the paper form with a computerized system, using handheld computers similar to those used for meter reading. Data regarding field work are entered into the handheld unit and uploaded to the data system at the end of each day.

A computer printout or written record, as shown in Figure 8-1, can also be used by the meter shop.

Mfr. No.	Co. No.	Make	Size
Date Purchased	Cost	Style	

INSTALLATION RECORD

Installed		Name	Address	Tap No.	Reasons for Removal	Removed	
Date	Reading					Date	Reading

TEST AND REPAIR RECORD

Date	Rate of Test			Repairs		Cost of Repair		Tested By	REMARKS
	Min. Flow	Inter. Flow	Max. Flow	% Accuracy Before Repair	% Accuracy After Repair	Mtl.	Labor		

Figure 8-1 Meter history record

PAPER METER RECORDS

Because increasingly more water utilities are using computers in their operation, it is logical that permanent records are kept in the electronic data system. Some utilities, however, still maintain some data in a paper record system. The data can be kept in a meter history report, as shown in Figure 8-2.

REPORT OF METER TEST AND REPAIRS

SHOP NO. ________________

SHOP NO. ________________

SIZE	MAKE	TYPE	NUMBER

METER READINGS	
AS RECEIVED	AFTER REPAIRS

REASON FOR TEST OR REPAIR					
STOPPED	FROZEN	LEAKING	TURN-OFF	COMPLAINT	PER. TEST
OTHER:					

DATE METER LAST RECONDITIONED

CONDITION AS RECEIVED				CONDITION AFTER REPAIRS			
	QUANTITY				QUANTITY		
RATED G.P.M. C.F.M.	NET WEIGHT	GALS. CU. FT.	RESULT (%)	RATED G.P.M. C.F.M.	NET WEIGHT	GALS. CU. FT.	RESULT (%)
REGISTER GEAR		SPINDLE GEAR		REGISTER GEAR		SPINDLE GEAR	

REPAIR PARTS USED

REPAIRED BY	DATE	TESTED BY	DATE

REMARKS

(FRONT)

Meter No. ________________

Meter Size ________________

Meter Make ________________

Date of Invoice ________________

RECORD			
Set			
Date	Service No.	Removed Date	Tested Date

(BACK)

Figure 8-2 Report of meter test and repairs

SUMMARY

A computerized system can provide a wealth of information when properly maintained. Although innumerable systems are used for maintaining meter records, any system should be able to provide all of the data the utility requires to monitor its operations. A review of almost any system of meter records will reveal duplications or more elaborate and detailed records than are needed. Addressing this problem will result in the elimination of unnecessary clerical work with only slight changes in the system or method. At a minimum, a systematic review will reveal whether current methods are being followed simply because "it's always been done that way."

Chapter 9

Remote Registration

HISTORY

Most of the water meters in North America are installed either in outdoor meter pits at some point along the service line or within a structure with limited access for the meter reader, such as in basements or utility closets. Water utilities have been using various remote-reading systems to improve meter-reading accuracy without having to gain access within structures or having to "dip out" water-flooded meter pits.

During the past 40 years, water utilities have seen meter reading evolve from manual entry readings in a route book to highly sophisticated, automatic meter-reading systems. Several important milestones marked this transformation from the basic manual system to the present-day, fully automatic systems.

The first was the development of a remote-reading system that eliminated both lock-out problems and potential liability issues when reading meters located indoors. The first widely used remote-reading system was introduced to the water industry in 1957. It consisted of a self-generating pulse register and a remotely located electromechanical register. After a specific amount of water was registered, a pulse was generated and sent to the remote register. Remote-reading systems utilizing encoder registers with plug-in remote reading followed, along with various hybrid remotes for water meters.

The next step in the evolutionary process was the introduction of handheld computers (data collectors) to allow meter readers to enter readings directly into a computer memory. Readings are transferred directly into the utility's computer billing system, thereby improving productivity, accuracy, information gathering, and customer service, while eliminating manual data-entry and shortening the read-to-bill cycle.

The next development was on-site automatic entry of the encoded meter reading into the handheld device (by probe, wand, or other device). By adding an adapter to the handheld computer, the meter reading and account number are obtained by inserting the adapter into a remotely located socket or by touching a pad connected to an encoder register on the water meter.

The final development was automatic meter reading (AMR) systems. These systems are fully automatic, with little or no human intervention, and data can be transmitted directly to a mobile collection device or a central location at the water utility. The communication link can be a telephone network, cable TV system, electrical power main, or a radio frequency (RF) based system.

Automatic meter reading is not new. It was introduced in the United States in the 1960s using network telephone systems as a communication link. What was new, however, was a wave of new technology, products, and systems for automatic meter reading using the public switched telephone network, the airwaves (radio frequency), and electric power mains to transmit data between the meter and the data collection computer.

CURRENT STATUS

As of 2012, over one-half of all the residential water meters sold in the United States were equipped for some form of AMR, and this includes a high percentage of commercial and industrial meters. Whereas early systems used cable or telephone networks, these have been surpassed by the ever-increasing use of radio frequency (RF). RF is employed via walk-by, drive-by mobile, and fixed network, which is most applicable for large systems. RF has now become the preferred "information highway" of AMR, and it is this area of the meter-reading process that is the most rapidly advancing technology in the water-utility industry.

RF networks have enjoyed such rapid growth because of their capability to provide benefits to the utility far beyond simple meter reading. Typical features include load profiling, tamper detection, leak detection, no-flow detection, reverse flow warnings, ease of special reads, elimination of estimated reads, and overall better customer service.

The availability of these features varies between systems and depends on the design details of the systems and their components. For this reason, it is impossible to provide specific details in this manual. It is recommended that utilities and other interested parties contact the various manufacturers for details on the features their systems provide.

Bibliography

American Society of Mechanical Engineers. 1910. River Discharge. New York: American Society of Mechanical Engineers.

ASME. 1937. *Fluid Meters.* 4th ed. New York: American Society of Mechanical Engineers.

ANSI/AWWA C510-07, Standard for Double Check Valve Backflow Prevention Assembly. Denver, Colo.: American Water Works Association.

ANSI/AWWA C511-07, Standard for Reduced-Pressure Principle Backflow Prevention Assembly. Denver, Colo.: American Water Works Association.

ANSI/AWWA C700-09, Standard for Cold-Water Meters—Displacement Type, Bronze Main Case. Denver, Colo.: American Water Works Association.

ANSI/AWWA C701-12, Standard for Cold-Water Meters—Turbine Type, for Customer Service. Denver, Colo.: American Water Works Association.

ANSI/AWWA C702-10, Standard for Cold-Water Meters—Compound Type. Denver, Colo.: American Water Works Association.

ANSI/AWWA C703-11, Standard for Cold-Water Meters—Fire-Service Type. Denver, Colo.: American Water Works Association.

ANSI/AWWA C704-08, Standard for Propeller-Type Meters for Waterworks Applications. Denver, Colo.: American Water Works Association.

ANSI/AWWA C706-10, Standard for Direct-Reading, Remote-Registration Systems for Cold-Water Meters. Denver, Colo.: American Water Works Association.

ANSI/AWWA C707-10, Standard for Encoder-Type Remote-Registration Systems for Cold-Water Meters. Denver, Colo.: American Water Works Association.

ANSI/AWWA C708-11, Standard for Cold-Water Meters—Multijet Type. Denver, Colo.: American Water Works Association.

ANSI/AWWA C710-09, Standard for Cold-Water Meters—Displacement Type, Plastic Main Case. Denver, Colo.: American Water Works Association.

ANSI/AWWA C712-10, Standard for Cold-Water Meters—Singlejet Type, Denver, Colo.: American Water Works Association.

ANSI/AWWA C713-10, Standard for Cold-Water Meters—Fluidic-Oscillator Type, Denver, Colo.: American Water Works Association.

AWWA Manual M22, *Sizing Water Service Lines and Meters.* Second Edition, 2004. Denver, Colo.: American Water Works Association.

Baker, R.C. 2000. *Flow Measurement Handbook: Industrial Designs, Operating Principles, Performance, and Applications,* Cambridge, UK: Cambridge University Press.

Browne, R.E. 1885. *Water Meters.* New York: D. Van Nostrand.

Frontinus, Sextus Julius. 1899. *The Two Books On the Water Supply of the City of Rome ..., A. D. 97...and Explanatory Chapters.* Trans. Clemens Herschel. Boston: D. Estes & Co.

National Institute of Standards and Technology. 2011. *Specifications, Tolerances, and Other Technical Requirements for Weighing and Measuring Devices.* Handbook 44. Gaithersburg, Md.: National Institute of Standards and Technology.

This page intentionally blank.

Index

NOTE: *f.* indicates a figure; *t.* indicates a table.

AWWA Manuals

M1, *Principles of Water Rates, Fees, and Charges*, Sixth Edition, 2012, #30001

M2, *Instrumentation and Control*, Third Edition, 2001, #30002

M3, *Safety Practices for Water Utilities*, Sixth Edition, 2002, #30003

M4, *Water Fluoridation Principles and Practices*, Fifth Edition, 2004, #30004

M5, *Water Utility Management*, Second Edition, 2004, #30005

M6, *Water Meters—Selection, Installation, Testing, and Maintenance*, Fifth Edition, 2012, #30006

M7, *Problem Organisms in Water: Identification and Treatment*, Third Edition, 2004, #30007

M9, *Concrete Pressure Pipe*, Third Edition, 2008, #30009

M11, *Steel Pipe—A Guide for Design and Installation*, Fifth Edition, 2004, #30011

M12, *Simplified Procedures for Water Examination*, Fifth Edition, 2002, #30012

M14, *Recommended Practice for Backflow Prevention and Cross-Connection Control*, Third Edition, 2003, #30014

M17, *Installation, Field Testing, and Maintenance of Fire Hydrants*, Fourth Edition, 2006, #30017

M19, *Emergency Planning for Water Utility Management*, Fourth Edition, 2001, #30019

M20, *Water Chlorination/Chloramination Practices and Principles*, Second Edition, 2006, #30020

M21, *Groundwater*, Third Edition, 2003, #30021

M22, *Sizing Water Service Lines and Meters*, Second Edition, 2004, #30022

M23, *PVC Pipe—Design and Installation*, Second Edition, 2003, #30023

M24, *Dual Water Systems*, Third Edition, 2009, #30024

M25, *Flexible-Membrane Covers and Linings for Potable-Water Reservoirs*, Third Edition, 2000, #30025

M27, *External Corrosion—Introduction to Chemistry and Control*, Second Edition, 2004, #30027

M28, *Rehabilitation of Water Mains*, Second Edition, 2001, #30028

M29, *Fundamentals of Water Utility Capital Financing*, Third Edition, 2008, #30029

M30, *Precoat Filtration*, Second Edition, 1995, #30030

M31, *Distribution System Requirements for Fire Protection*, Fourth Edition, 2008, #30031

M32, *Computer Modeling of Water Distribution Systems*, Third Edition, 2012, #30032

M33, *Flowmeters in Water Supply*, Second Edition, 2006, #30033

M36, *Water Audits and Loss Control Programs*, Third Edition, 2009, #30036

M37, *Operational Control of Coagulation and Filtration Processes*, Third Edition, 2011, #30037

M38, *Electrodialysis and Electrodialysis Reversal*, First Edition, 1995, #30038

M41, *Ductile-Iron Pipe and Fittings*, Third Edition, 2009, #30041

M42, *Steel Water-Storage Tanks*, First Edition, 1998, #30042

M44, *Distribution Valves: Selection, Installation, Field Testing, and Maintenance*, Second Edition, 2006, #30044

M45, *Fiberglass Pipe Design*, Second Edition, 2005, #30045

M46, *Reverse Osmosis and Nanofiltration*, Second Edition, 2007, #30046

M47, *Capital Project Delivery*, Second Edition, 2010, #30047

M48, *Waterborne Pathogens*, Second Edition, 2006, #30048

M49, *Butterfly Valves: Torque, Head Loss, and Cavitation Analysis*, Second Edition, 2012, #30049

M50, *Water Resources Planning*, Second Edition, 2007, #30050

M51, *Air-Release, Air/Vacuum, and Combination Air Valves*, First Edition, 2001, #30051

M52, *Water Conservation Programs—A Planning Manual*, First Edition, 2006, #30052

M53, *Microfiltration and Ultrafiltration Membranes for Drinking Water*, First Edition, 2005, #30053

M54, *Developing Rates for Small Systems*, First Edition, 2004, #30054

M55, *PE Pipe—Design and Installation*, First Edition, 2006, #30055

M56, *Fundamentals and Control of Nitrification in Chloraminated Drinking Water Distribution Systems*, First Edition, 2006, #30056

M57, *Algae: Source to Treatment*, First Edition, 2010, #30057

M58, *Internal Corrosion Control in Water Distribution Systems*, First Edition, 2011, #30058

M60, *Drought Preparedness and Response,* First Edition, 2011, #30060

M61, *Desalination of Seawater,* First Edition, 2011, #30061

CPSIA information can be obtained at www.ICGtesting.com
Printed in the USA
BVOW04s1504190515

400996BV00004B/25/P

9 781583 218624